C000067954

Maths Revision
Higher Level
Paper 2

Brendan Guildea, Louise Boylan & George Humphrey

Gill & Macmillan

Gill & Macmillan

Hume Avenue

Park West

Dublin 12

www.gillmacmillan.ie

© Brendan Guildea, Louise Boylan and George Humphrey 2013

978 07171 4693 2

Any links to external websites should not be construed as an endorsement by Gill &
Macmillan of the content or view of the linked material.

For permission to reproduce photographs, the authors and publisher gratefully
acknowledge the following:

© Alamy: 104, 128,133, 214, 215; © Getty Images: 97; © Shutterstock: 84, 91, 140,
143, 149; © Shutterstock / Michael Winston Rosa: 3.

The authors and publisher have made every effort to trace all copyright holders, but if
any has been inadvertently overlooked we would be pleased to make the necessary
arrangement at the first opportunity.

Acknowledgements

The authors would like to thank Colm Kelleher, Elaine Guildea, Joe Heron and Colman
Humphrey who helped with the proofreading, checked the answers and made valuable
suggestions that are included in the final text.

CONTENTS

Please note:

- The philosophy of Project Maths is that topics can overlap, so you may encounter Paper 1 material on Paper 2 and vice versa.
- The Exam questions marked by the symbol 🔵 in this book are selected from the following:
  1. SEC Exam papers
  2. Sample exam papers
  3. Original and sourced exam-type questions

Introduction

aims

- [ ] To learn how to revise most effectively
- [ ] To familiarise yourself with the structure of the exam paper
- [ ] To learn how to allocate the correct time for each question
- [ ] To know and understand the words which appear often on the exam paper
- [ ] To familiarise yourself with the syllabus

The aim of this revision book is to help you enhance your grade in your Leaving Certificate. The book is designed to be exam focused. To do this, the book is based not just on the syllabus, but also on the examination paper. Because of this, this revision book can be used in conjunction with **any** textbook.

Throughout this book, **examples and exam-type questions are graded by level of difficulty**.

This level of difficulty is indicated by calculator symbols, as follows:

The number of calculators shown beside a question helps you know how difficult the question is. One calculator indicates a question which is relatively basic. As the questions get harder, there will be more calculators. Three calculators indicates an average-level question, whereas five calculators indicates that it is a very challenging question. These questions may be beyond some students, but give them a go! **Students hoping to achieve an A grade should aim to complete all of the five calculator questions. The calculator symbol given for each question relates to the most difficult part of that question. Don't be discouraged by a challenging question.** As in the Leaving Certificate exam, difficult questions can sometimes begin with one or two simple parts. You should attempt as much as you can.

It is very important to realise that **you are your own best teacher**. Revision is when you begin to teach yourself. Thus, it is very important for you to start your revision as soon as possible. Make notes while you are revising. If you are having difficulty with a particular question, seek help from your teacher, a friend or a member of your family. As with all subjects, the best examination preparation is to work through past examination or sample papers so that you are familiar with the layout and the style of questions.

Let's start at the beginning. If you want to do well in your Leaving Certificate, then two things are essential:

- Revise effectively.
- Be familiar with the exam paper and so be prepared on the day of the exam.

These may seem obvious, but it's worth taking a moment to think about what these tips mean.

How to revise most effectively

If you are going to do well in the Leaving Certificate, you need to spend quite a bit of time revising. Spending a little time learning how to revise effectively will help you get more from your time and will help you absorb and understand more of the material on the course. Here are some tips to help you revise for maths.

- Find a quiet place where you can work. This place should be dedicated to study and free of potential distractions. Turn off the TV, computer and mobile phone.
- Write a study plan. Don't be afraid to ask your parents/teachers/guidance counsellor for help at this stage.
- Do the more challenging revision first, when you are fresh. Trying to focus on difficult problems when you are tired can be counter-productive.
- Project Maths is based on understanding, so while you can 'learn' some elements of the course, it is important that you develop an understanding of the material.
- Drill and practice are essential ingredients for success in maths.
- Try to link any new material to things you know already. This is learning through association and helps long-term retention.

Study in small chunks of time lasting 25 to 35 minutes. Your memory and concentration will work better if you study in short, frequent bursts.

Don't get hung up on more difficult material. Concentrate on understanding the fundamental concepts and being able to answer all straightforward questions. Then, with time, you can build up to the more challenging problems.

Leaving Certificate examination

Exam focus is critical to exam success. It is important to prepare yourself for the challenges you will face. By learning about the structure of the exam, you will learn how to maximise your points, allocate your time effectively and manage the paper in a calm manner.

The examination paper will be presented in two sections.

Section A – 150 marks
Concepts and Skills

Read the exam paper right through at the start in order to determine which question is the easiest one to start with. Your mind may also be subconsciously processing some of the other problems.

Section B – 150 marks
Contexts and Applications

Start with your best question, then your next best and so on. This way, if you are short of time, at least your best questions will be done.

Time yourself as follows

- Read the paper at the start: 5 minutes
- Section A: 70 minutes
- Section B: 70 minutes
- Review your answers at the end: 5 minutes
- Try to stick closely to these times. If you run out of time on a question, leave it and come back at the end.
- Keep moving through the questions and follow the procedures you have learned.

Attempt marks are valuable, so it is vital that you attempt all questions. Leave **NO** blanks.

Further exam tips

- There is no such thing as rough work in Maths – all work is relevant. If the examiner doesn't know how you reached an answer, even a correct answer, then full marks may not be awarded. Thus, **show all your work**.
- Attempt marks will be awarded for any step in the right direction. Therefore, **make an attempt at each part of the question**. Even if you do not get the correct answer, you can still pick up most of the marks on offer if you show how you worked it out. Also, **draw a diagram where possible** because this can help you see the solution.
- If you cannot finish part of a question, leave a space and come back to it later. **Never scribble out any work or use Tipp-Ex**. Put a single line through it so that the examiner can still read it. In many cases, work that had a line through it received more marks. **Avoid using pencil** because the writing can be very faint and difficult to read.

- It is a good idea to show each stage of a calculation when using a calculator (in case you press a wrong key). Familiarise yourself with your calculator. Know your book of tables and formulae well and write down any formula that you use.

key point

Your calculator and book of tables are two extremely valuable resources to have in the exam. Make sure that you are very familiar with how your calculator works and that you know how to perform all functions on it. Also familiarise yourself with the book of tables so that you don't waste any time in the exam trying to find formulae.

Glossary of words used on the examination paper

Write down, state
You can write down your answer without showing any work. However, if you want you can show some workings.

Calculate, find, show that, determine, prove
Obtain your answers by showing all relevant work. Marks are available for showing the steps leading to your final answer or conclusion.

Solve
Find the solution, or root, of an equation. The solution is the value of the variable that makes the left-hand side balance with the right-hand side.

Evaluate
Work out, or find, a numerical value by putting in numbers for letters.

Comment on
After studying the given information or answers, give your opinion on their significance.

Plot
Indicate the position of points on a graph, usually on the x- and y-planes.

Construct
Draw an accurate diagram, usually labelled, using a pencil, ruler, set square, compass and protractor. Leave all constructions on your diagram.

Sketch
Make a rough diagram or graph, labelled if needed.

Hence
You **must** use the answer, or result, from the previous part of the question.

Hence or otherwise
It is recommended that you use the answer, or result, from the previous part of the question, and it is usually best to do this, but other methods are acceptable.

Syllabus checklist for Leaving Certificate Higher Level Maths Paper 2 exam

The philosophy of Project Maths is that topics can overlap, so you may encounter Paper 1 material on Paper 2 and vice versa.

The syllabus stresses that in all aspects of the Leaving Certificate Maths course, students should be able to:

- ☐ Explore patterns and formulate conjectures
- ☐ Explain findings
- ☐ Justify conclusions
- ☐ Communicate mathematics verbally and in written form
- ☐ Apply their knowledge and skills to solve problems in familiar and unfamiliar contexts
- ☐ Analyse information presented verbally and translate it into mathematical form
- ☐ Devise, select and use appropriate mathematical models, formulae or techniques to process information and to draw relevant conclusions

Coordinate geometry of the line

- ☐ Use slopes to show that two lines are:
  - ○ parallel
  - ○ perpendicular.
- ☐ Recognise the fact that the relationship $ax + by + c = 0$ is linear.
- ☐ Solve problems involving slopes of lines.
- ☐ Calculate the area of a triangle.
- ☐ Solve problems involving:
  - ○ the perpendicular distance from a point to a line
  - ○ the angle between two lines.
- ☐ Divide a line segment internally in a given ratio $m : n$.

Coordinate geometry of the circle

- ☐ Recognise that $(x - h)^2 + (y - k)^2 = r^2$ represents the relationship between the x and y coordinates of points on a circle with centre (h, k) and radius r.
- ☐ Recognise that $x^2 + y^2 + 2gx + 2fy + c = 0$ represents the relationship between the x and y coordinates of points on a circle with centre $(-g, -f)$ and radius r where $r = \sqrt{g^2 + f^2 - c}$.
- ☐ Solve problems involving a line and a circle.

Trigonometry

- ☐ Use the theorem of Pythagoras to solve problems.
- ☐ Define $\sin \theta$, $\cos \theta$ and $\tan \theta$ for all values of θ.
- ☐ Work with trigonometric ratios in surd form.
- ☐ Use trigonometry to calculate the area of a triangle.
- ☐ Solve problems using the sine and cosine rules.
- ☐ Solve problems involving the area of a sector of a circle and the length of an arc.
- ☐ Use trigonometry to solve problems in 3D.
- ☐ Graph the trigonometric functions sine, cosine, tangent.
- ☐ Graph trigonometric functions of type $f(\theta) = a + b\sin c\theta$ and $g(\theta) = a + b\cos c\theta$ for $a, b, c \in \mathbb{R}$.
- ☐ Solve trigonometric equations such as $\sin n\theta = 0$ and $\cos n\theta = \dfrac{1}{2}$, giving all solutions.
- ☐ Use the radian measure of angles.
- ☐ Derive the trigonometric formulae 1, 2, 3, 4, 5, 6, 7, 9.
- ☐ Apply the trigonometric formulae 1–24 .

Geometry

Synthetic geometry

- ☐ Perform constructions 1–22.
- ☐ Construct $\sqrt{2}$ and $\sqrt{3}$ geometrically.
- ☐ Use the following terms related to logic and deductive reasoning:

    theorem, proof, axiom, corollary, converse, implies, is equivalent to, if and only if, proof by contradiction

- ☐ Investigate theorems 7, 8, 11, 12, 13, 16, 17, 18, 20, 21 and corollary 6 and use them to solve problems.
- ☐ Prove theorems 11, 12, 13.

Transformation geometry, enlargements

- ☐ Investigate enlargements, paying attention to:
  - ○ centre of enlargement
  - ○ scale factor k, where $0 < k < 1$, $k \in \mathbb{Q}$
  - ○ scale factor k, $k > 1$, $k \in \mathbb{Q}$
  - ○ area.
- ☐ Solve problems involving enlargements.

Length, area and volume

- ☐ Select and use suitable strategies to find:
  - ○ the length of the perimeter and the area of the following plane figures: parallelogram, trapezium and figures made from combinations of these
  - ○ surface area and volume of the following solid figures: cylinder, right cone, right prism and sphere.
- ☐ Use the trapezoidal rule to approximate area.
- ☐ Investigate the nets of prisms (polygonal bases), cylinders and cones.
- ☐ Solve problems involving the length of the perimeter and the area of the following plane figures: disc, triangle, rectangle, square, parallelogram, trapezium, sectors of discs and figures made from combinations of these.
- ☐ Solve problems involving surface area and volume of the following solid figures: rectangular block, cylinder, right cone, triangular-based prism (right angle, isosceles and equilateral), sphere, hemisphere and solids made from combinations of these.

Probability

Counting

- ☐ List outcomes of an experiment.
- ☐ Apply the fundamental principles of counting.
- ☐ Count the arrangements of n distinct objects ($n!$).
- ☐ Count the number of ways of arranging r objects from n distinct objects (nPr).
- ☐ Count the number of ways of selecting r objects from n distinct objects (nCr).

Concepts of probability

- ☐ Decide whether an everyday event is likely or unlikely to occur.
- ☐ Recognise that probability is a measure on a scale of 0–1 of how likely an event is to occur.
- ☐ Use set theory; discuss experiments, outcomes, sample spaces.
- ☐ Use the language of probability to discuss events, including those with equally likely outcomes.
- ☐ Estimate probabilities from experimental data.
- ☐ Recognise that if an experiment is repeated, there will be different outcomes and that increasing the number of times an experiment is repeated generally leads to better estimates of probability.
- ☐ Associate the probability of an event with its long-run relative frequency.
- ☐ Discuss basic rules of probability (and/or, mutually exclusive) through the use of Venn diagrams.

☐ Calculate expected value and understand that this does not need to be one of the outcomes.

☐ Recognise the role of expected value in decision-making and explore the issue of fair games.

☐ Extend your understanding of the basic rules of probability (and/or, mutually exclusive) through the use of formulae:

   ○ addition rule: $P(A \cup B) = P(A) + P(B) - P(A \cap B)$

   ○ multiplication rule (independent events): $P(A \cap B) = P(A) \times P(B)$

   ○ multiplication rule (general case): $P(A \cap B) = P(A) \times P(B \mid A)$

☐ Solve problems involving conditional probability in a systematic way.

☐ Appreciate that in general, $P(A \mid B) \neq P(B \mid A)$.

☐ Examine the implications of $P(A \mid B) \neq P(B \mid A)$ in context.

Outcomes of random processes

☐ Construct sample spaces for two independent events.

☐ Apply the principle that in the case of equally likely outcomes, the probability is given by the number of outcomes of interest divided by the total number of outcomes (examples using coins, dice, spinners, urns with coloured objects, playing cards, etc.).

☐ Find the probability that two independent events both occur.

☐ Apply an understanding of Bernoulli trials.

☐ Solve problems involving up to three Bernoulli trials.

☐ Calculate the probability that the first success occurs on the nth Bernoulli trial where n is specified.

☐ Solve problems involving calculating the probability of k successes in n repeated Bernoulli trials (normal approximation not required).

☐ Calculate the probability that the kth success occurs on the nth Bernoulli trial.

☐ Use simulations to explore the variability of sample statistics from a known population, to construct sampling distributions and to draw conclusions about the sampling distribution of the mean.

☐ Solve problems involving reading probabilities from the normal distribution tables.

Statistics
Statistical reasoning with an aim of becoming a statistically aware consumer

☐ Engage in discussions about the purpose of statistics and recognise misconceptions and misuses of statistics.

☐ Discuss populations and samples.

☐ Decide to what extent conclusions can be generalised.

☐ Work with different types of data – categorical, nominal or ordinal numerical, discrete or continuous – in order to clarify the problem at hand.

☐ Work with different types of bivariate data.

Finding, collecting and organising data

☐ Clarify the problem at hand.

☐ Formulate one (or more) questions that can be answered with data.

☐ Explore different ways of collecting data.

☐ Generate data or source data from other sources, including the internet.

☐ Select a sample (simple random sample).

☐ Recognise the importance of representativeness so as to avoid biased samples.

☐ Discuss different types of studies: sample surveys, observational studies and designed experiments.

☐ Recognise the importance of randomisation and the role of the control group in studies.

☐ Recognise biases, limitations and ethical issues of each type of study.

☐ Select a random sample (know the definitions of stratified, cluster, quota).

☐ Design a plan and collect data on the basis of the above knowledge.

Representing data graphically and numerically

Graphical:

☐ Describe the sample (both univariate and bivariate data) by selecting appropriate graphical or numerical methods.

☐ Evaluate the effectiveness of different displays in representing the findings of a statistical investigation conducted by others.

☐ Use stem and leaf plots and histograms (equal intervals) to display data.

☐ Explore the distribution of data, including concepts of symmetry and skewness.

☐ Compare data sets using appropriate displays, including back-to-back stem and leaf plots.

☐ Determine the relationship between variables using scatterplots.

☐ Recognise that correlation is a value from -1 to $+1$ and that it measures the extent of the linear relationship between two variables.

☐ Match correlation coefficient values to appropriate scatterplots.

☐ Understand that correlation does not imply causality.

☐ Analyse plots of the data to explain differences in measures of centre and spread.

☐ Draw the line of best fit by eye.

☐ Make predictions based on the line of best fit.

☐ Calculate the correlation coefficient by calculator.

Numerical:

☐ Use a variety of summary statistics to describe the data:
  ○ central tendency: mean, median, mode
  ○ variability: range.

☐ Recognise standard deviation and interquartile range as measures of variability.

☐ Use a calculator to calculate standard deviation.

☐ Find quartiles and the interquartile range.

☐ Use the interquartile range appropriately when analysing data.

☐ Recognise the existence and the effect of outliers.

☐ Use percentiles to assign relative standing.

Analysing, interpreting and drawing inferences from data

☐ Recognise how sampling variability influences the use of sample information to make statements about the population.

☐ Use appropriate tools to describe variability, drawing inferences about the population from the sample.

☐ Interpret the analysis.

☐ Relate the interpretation to the original question.

☐ Interpret a histogram in terms of the distribution of data.

☐ Make decisions based on the empirical rule.

☐ Recognise the concept of a hypothesis test.

☐ Calculate the margin of error for a population proportion.

☐ Conduct a hypothesis test on a population proportion using the margin of error.

1 ▸ Coordinate Geometry of the Line

 aims

☐ To know where to find the coordinate geometry formulae in the booklet of formulae and tables

☐ To learn how to apply these formulae to procedural and in-context examination questions

☐ To gain the ability, with practice, to recall relevant techniques and tactics for the exam

Example

When geese fly in formation, they form an inverted V-shape.

(i) If the lines of geese can be represented by the equations $x + 2y - 10 = 0$ and $3x - 2y - 6 = 0$, find the coordinates of the leading goose.

(ii) After 1 hour, the leading goose has flown to a point $(37, 67)$.
Assuming the geese flew in a straight line and taking each unit to represent 1 km, find the distance travelled by the geese to the nearest km.

(iii) Hence, find the average flying speed in m/s.

Solution

(i) $\quad x + 2y - 10 = 0$

$\quad\;\; \underline{3x - 2y - 6 = 0}$

$\quad 4x - 16 = 0$

$\qquad\qquad\quad 4x = 16$

$\qquad\qquad\quad\; x = 4$

Sub $x = 4$ $\quad$ into $\quad\; x + 2y - 10 = 0$

$\qquad\qquad$ To get $\quad 4 + 2y - 10 = 0$

$\qquad\qquad\qquad\qquad\quad 2y - 6 = 0$

$\qquad\qquad\qquad\qquad\qquad\; 2y = 6$

$\qquad\qquad\qquad\qquad\qquad\;\; y = 3$

Leading goose position is $(4, 3)$.

(ii) Distance $= \sqrt{(x_2 - x_1)^2 + (y_2 - y_1)^2}$ (see booklet of formulae and tables page 18)

$(x_1, y_1) = (4, 3)$

$(x_2, y_2) = (37, 67)$

Distance $= \sqrt{(37 - 4)^2 + (67 - 3)^2}$

$= \sqrt{1{,}089 + 4{,}096}$

$= \sqrt{5{,}185}$

$= 72 \cdot 00694411$

Distance to the nearest km $= 72$ km

(iii) Speed $= \dfrac{\text{Distance}}{\text{Time}} = \dfrac{72 \times 1{,}000}{60 \times 60} = 20$ m/sec

key point

This example is a revision of material from the Junior Certificate.

Example

The table shows temperatures in Celsius and the equivalent Fahrenheit.

Celsius (C)	50	65	80	95	100	120
Fahrenheit (F)	122	149	176	203	212	248

(i) Using a graph, investigate whether these values form a linear relationship.

(ii) Find this relationship in the form $F = aC + b$, where $a, b \in \mathbb{R}$ and C, F represent the temperature in Celsius and Fahrenheit, respectively.

(iii) Use this relationship to find the equivalent Fahrenheit temperature for $-30°C$.

Solution

(i)

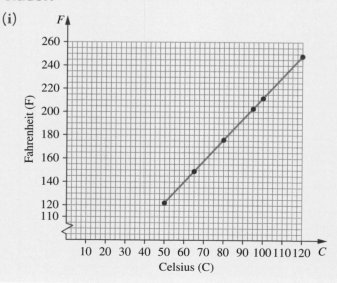

Celsius (C)

The graph seems linear

(ii) To find the equation of the line, we need its slope and one point on it.

To find the slope, we use the two extreme points: $(50, 122)$ and $(120, 248)$.

$$\text{Slope} = m = \frac{y_2 - y_1}{x_2 - x_1} \quad \text{(see booklet of formulae and tables page 18)}$$

$$= \frac{248 - 122}{120 - 50} = \frac{126}{70} = \frac{9}{5} \text{ or } 1{\cdot}8$$

Equation of a line: $y - y_1 = m(x - x_1)$ (see booklet of formulae and tables page 18)

$$F - 122 = \frac{9}{5}(C - 50)$$

$$F - 122 = \frac{9}{5}C - 90$$

$$F = \frac{9}{5}C - 90 + 122$$

$$F = \frac{9}{5}C + 32$$

(iii) $F = \dfrac{9}{5}(-30) + 32 = -54 + 32 = -22$

Thus $-30°\text{C} = -22°\text{F}$

Slope of a line

Slope of a line, m, given two points.

$$m = \frac{y_2 - y_1}{x_2 - x_1}$$

Slope is $\dfrac{\text{rise}}{\text{run}} = \tan \theta$, where θ is the angle the line makes with the positive sense of the x-axis.

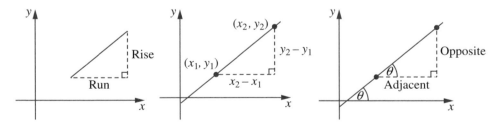

We say θ, the angle of inclination, is the angle formed between a line and the positive side of the x-axis.

The angle of inclination is always between $0°$ and $180°$.

- It is always measured anticlockwise from the positive side of the x-axis.
- The slope m of any line is equal to the tangent of its angle of inclination:
  then $m = \tan \theta$ (where $\theta = $ angle of inclination).

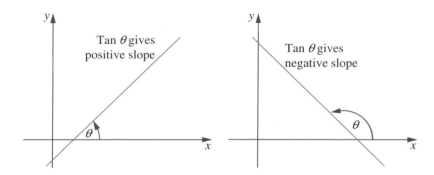

Lines parallel to the axes

$y = 1$ is a line parallel to the x-axis through the point $(0, 1)$.

$x = 2$ is a line parallel to the y-axis through the point $(2, 0)$.

key point

$y = 0$ is the equation of the x-axis.
$x = 0$ is the equation of the y-axis.

All horizontal lines have an angle of inclination of $0°$.

Their slopes are zero.

All vertical lines have an angle of inclination of $90°$.

Their slopes are infinitely steep.

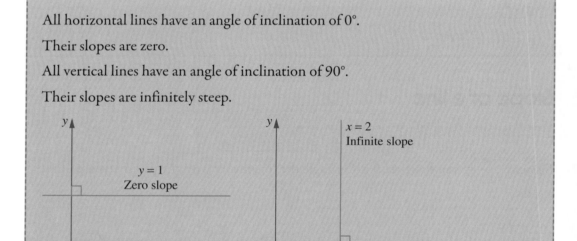

Transformations of the plane

(a) Translation: A translation moves a point in a straight line.

(b) Central symmetry: Central symmetry is a reflection in a point.

(c) Axial symmetry: Axial symmetry is a reflection in a line.

(d) Axial symmetry in the axes or central symmetry in the origin.

Note: Under a translation or a central symmetry, a line is mapped onto a parallel line.

Example

Investigate whether $A(-4, 3)$, $B(-1, 6)$ and $C(7, 10)$ are collinear.

Collinear: If three or more points lie on the same line, then the points are said to be collinear.
Note: Two points always lie on a line.

Solution

Method 1

The three points either form a straight line or they do not.
To decide which, we will find the slopes of AB and BC.

$$m_{AB} = \frac{y_2 - y_1}{x_2 - x_1} \qquad\qquad m_{BC} = \frac{y_2 - y_1}{x_2 - x_1}$$

$$= \frac{6 - 3}{-1 - (-4)} = \frac{3}{3} = 1 \qquad\qquad = \frac{10 - 6}{7 - (-1)} = \frac{4}{8} = \frac{1}{2}$$

As $m_{AB} \neq m_{BC}$, the points A, B and C are not collinear.
Note: We could have found the slope of m_{AC} as one of the two slopes.

Method 2

To find the area of $\triangle ABC$, use translation $(-4, 3) \rightarrow (0, 0)$ to get:

$$A = (-4, 3) \rightarrow (0, 0) \qquad\qquad \text{(Add 4 to } x\text{, subtract 3 from } y\text{)}$$
$$B = (-1, 6) \rightarrow (3, 3) = (x_1, y_1)$$
$$C = (7, 10) \rightarrow (11, 7) = (x_2, y_2)$$

$\therefore$ Area $\triangle ABC = \dfrac{1}{2}|x_1y_2 - x_2y_1|$ (see booklet of formulae and tables page 18)

$$= \frac{1}{2}|(3)(7) - (11)(3)|$$

$$= \frac{1}{2}|21 - 33| = \frac{1}{2}|-12| = 6$$

Since the area of $\triangle ABC \neq 0$, the three points A, B and C do not form a straight line $\Rightarrow A, B$ and C are not collinear.

key point

If the area of $\triangle PQR = 0$, then we can state P, Q, R are collinear.

Division of a line segment in a given ratio

The coordinates of the point $C(x, y)$ which divides the line segment $P(x_1, y_1)$ and $Q(x_2, y_2)$ internally in the ratio $a : b$ is given by:

Internal divisor

(see booklet of formulae and tables page 18)

$$C(x, y) = \left(\frac{bx_1 + ax_2}{b + a}, \frac{by_1 + ay_2}{b + a} \right)$$

Example

(i) $P(7, -11)$ and $Q(-5, 5)$ are two points. C is a point on $[PQ]$ such that $|PC| : |CQ| = 5 : 3$. Find the coordinates of C.

(ii) The point $R\left(-\frac{1}{2}, -1\right)$ divides the line segment $|VW|$ such that $|VR| : |RW| = 1 : 4$. If the coordinates of V are $(3, -3)$, find the coordinates of W.

Solution

(i) $C = \left(\dfrac{(5)(-5) + (3)(7)}{5 + 3}, \dfrac{(5)(5) + (3)(-11)}{5 + 3} \right)$

$C = \left(\dfrac{-25 + 21}{8}, \dfrac{25 - 33}{8} \right) = \left(-\dfrac{1}{2}, -1 \right)$

(ii) Using a translation

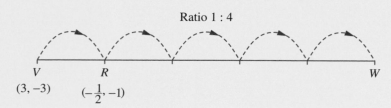

Ratio $1 : 4$

V $\qquad$ R $\qquad$ W

$(3, -3)$ $\qquad$ $\left(-\frac{1}{2}, -1\right)$

Notice translation $V \rightarrow R$ means $(3, -3) \rightarrow \left(-\frac{1}{2}, -1\right)$

x-component $-3\frac{1}{2}$

y-component $+2$

V R W

$\left(-\frac{1}{2}, -1\right)$

x-component $-\frac{1}{2} - 3\frac{1}{2} - 3\frac{1}{2} - 3\frac{1}{2} - 3\frac{1}{2} = -14\frac{1}{2}$

y-component $-1 + 2 + 2 + 2 + 2 = 7$

$$W = \left(-14\frac{1}{2}, 7\right)$$

(i) The line $4x - 5y + k = 0$ cuts the x-axis at P and the y-axis at Q. Write down the coordinates of P and Q in terms of k.

(ii) The area of the triangle OPQ is 10 square units, where O is the origin. Find two possible values of k.

Solution

(i) P is on the x-axis $\Rightarrow y = 0$

$$4x - 5y + k = 0$$
$$4x - 5(0) + k = 0$$
$$x = -\frac{k}{4}$$

Thus, P has coordinates $\left(-\frac{k}{4}, 0\right)$.

Q is on the y-axis $\Rightarrow x = 0$

$$4x - 5y + k = 0$$
$$4(0) - 5y + k = 0$$
$$y = \frac{k}{5}$$

Thus, Q has coordinates $\left(0, \frac{k}{5}\right)$.

(ii) Points: $(0, 0)$, $\left(-\frac{k}{4}, 0\right)$, $\left(0, \frac{k}{5}\right)$ Given: area of $\triangle OPQ = 10$

$$\text{Area of } \triangle = \frac{1}{2}\left|x_1 y_2 - x_2 y_1\right| = 10$$

$$\frac{1}{2}\left|\left(-\frac{k}{4}\right)\left(\frac{k}{5}\right) - (0)(0)\right| = 10 \quad \text{(multiply by 2)}$$

$$\left|-\frac{k^2}{20}\right| = 20$$

$$-\frac{k^2}{20} = 20 \text{ or } -\frac{k^2}{20} = -20$$

$$k^2 = -400 \text{ or } k^2 = 400$$

Reject $\qquad k = \pm 20$

key point

k^2 is always positive where $k \in R$, hence we reject $k^2 = -400$.

Concurrencies of a triangle

1. Centroid G

A **median** of a triangle is a line segment from a vertex to the midpoint of the opposite side. The three medians of a triangle meet at a point called the centroid, G. G divides each median in the ratio $2 : 1$.

Coordinates of $G = \left(\dfrac{x_1 + x_2 + x_3}{3}, \dfrac{y_1 + y_2 + y_3}{3} \right)$.

(see booklet of formulae and tables page 52)

exam focus

The following three geometry constructions using concurrencies may be easily incorporated into a coordinate geometry exam question. They are worth remembering.

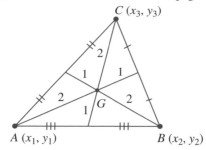

key point

The centre of gravity of a triangular lamina is at its centroid.

2. Circumcentre O

The circumcentre of a triangle is the point of intersection of the perpendicular bisectors of the sides.

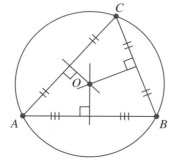

3. Orthocentre H

An altitude of a triangle is a perpendicular line from a vertex to its opposite side. The orthocentre is the point of intersection of the altitudes.

Note: The centroid, circumcentre and orthocentre in a triangle all lie on a straight line called **Euler's line.**

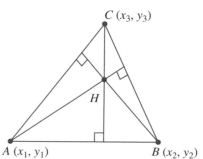

Example

$P(7, 3)$ and $Q(-1, -5)$ are two points. R is the midpoint of $[PQ]$. Find the values of t if the line containing the point R and $S(t^2, t)$ is perpendicular to PQ.

Solution

We have two methods to find R.

Method 1: Average

$P(7, 3)$

$\underline{Q(-1, -5)}$

$(6, -2)$ (add)

$R(3, -1)$ (divide by 2)

Method 2: Formula

$$\text{Midpoint} = \left(\frac{x_1 + x_2}{2}, \frac{y_1 + y_2}{2} \right)$$

$$= \left(\frac{7 - 1}{2}, \frac{3 - 5}{2} \right)$$

$$R = (3, -1)$$

We have an equation in disguise, based on slopes, to find the values of t.

$$m = \frac{y_2 - y_1}{x_2 - x_1}$$

$$PQ: \quad m_1 = \frac{-5 - 3}{-1 - 7}$$

$$= \frac{-8}{-8}$$

$$m_1 = 1$$

$$m = \frac{y_2 - y_1}{x_2 - x_1}$$

$$RS: \quad m_2 = \frac{t - (-1)}{t^2 - 3}$$

$$m_2 = \frac{t + 1}{t^2 - 3}$$

$$PQ \perp RS$$

$$m_1 \times m_2 = -1$$

$$(1)\left(\frac{t + 1}{t^2 - 3} \right) = -1$$

$$\frac{t + 1}{t^2 - 3} = -1$$

$$t + 1 = -1(t^2 - 3)$$

$$t + 1 = -t^2 + 3$$

$$t^2 + t - 2 = 0$$

$$(t + 2)(t - 1) = 0$$

$$t = -2 \text{ or } t = 1$$

key point

To prove whether or not two lines are perpendicular, do the following.

1. Find the slope of each line.
2. Multiply both slopes.
3. (i) If the answer in step 2 is -1, the lines are perpendicular.

   (ii) If the answer in step 2 is not -1, the lines are not perpendicular.

Note:

$bx - ay + k = 0$ is a line perpendicular to the line $ax + by + c = 0$.

key point

Parallel lines have equal slopes. If $l_1 \parallel l_2$, then $m_1 = m_2$.

Conversely, if two lines have equal slopes, then they are parallel.

Note:

$ax + by + k = 0$ is a line parallel to the line $ax + by + c = 0$.

Perpendicular distance from a point to a line

The perpendicular distance, d, from the point (x_1, y_1) to the line $ax + by + c = 0$ is given by:

$$d = \frac{|ax_1 + by_1 + c|}{\sqrt{a^2 + b^2}}$$

(see booklet of formulae and tables page 19)

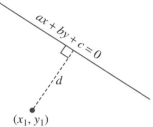

A ship is 10 km due south of a lighthouse at noon.

The ship is travelling at 15 km/h on a bearing of θ, as shown below, where $\theta = \tan^{-1}\dfrac{4}{3}$.

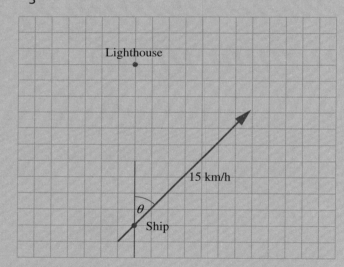

(i) On the diagram above, draw a set of coordinate axes that takes the lighthouse as the origin, the line east–west through the lighthouse as the x-axis and kilometres as units.

(ii) Find the equation of the line along which the ship is moving.

(iii) Find the shortest distance between the ship and the lighthouse during the journey.

(iv) At what time is the ship closest to the lighthouse?

This question contains all the basic ingredients examiners like to use:

(a) Apply a simple diagram.

(b) Requires a standard formula but with a twist. In this case, $m \neq \tan\theta$, since θ is not the angle in the positive direction.

(c) Apply a more advanced formula.

(d) To make the candidate think and use some techniques from other topics. In this instance, speed and time and Pythagoras' theorem.

Solution

(i)

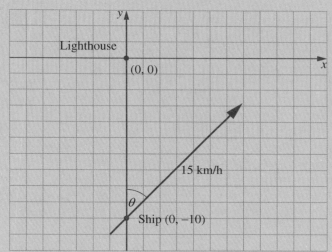

(ii)

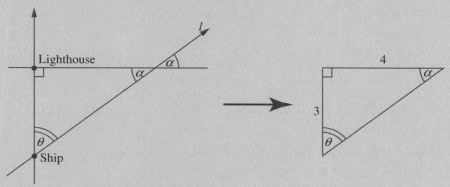

Given $\theta = \tan^{-1}\left(\dfrac{4}{3}\right)$

Then $\tan\theta = \dfrac{4}{3}$

Hence, $\tan \alpha = \dfrac{3}{4}$

The slope of line l is given by

$m = \tan \alpha = \dfrac{3}{4}$

The equation of l is given by
$y - y_1 = m(x - x_1)$

$(x_1, y_1) = (0, -10)$

$$y - (-10) = \dfrac{3}{4}(x - 0)$$

$$4y + 40 = 3x$$

$$4y - 3x + 40 = 0$$

(iii) The shortest distance is given by the perpendicular distance.

Perpendicular distance $= \left| \dfrac{ax_1 + by_1 + c}{\sqrt{a^2 + b^2}} \right|$

$(x_1, y_1) = (0, 0)$

$a = -3$

$b = 4$

$c = 40$

Shortest distance $= \dfrac{|(-3)(0) + (4)(0) + 40|}{\sqrt{(-3)^2 + (4)^2}}$

$= \dfrac{0 + 0 + 40}{\sqrt{9 + 16}} = 8 \text{ km}$

• $(0, 0)$

l

$-3x + 4y + 40 = 0$

(iv)

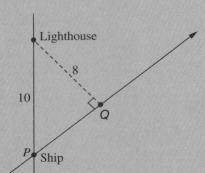

To find $|PQ|$, use the theorem of Pythagoras:

$(10)^2 = (8)^2 + |PQ|^2$

$100 = 64 + |PQ|^2$

$36 = |PQ|^2$

$6 \text{ km} = |PQ|$

Time required by the ship to travel 6 km given by:

Time $= \dfrac{\text{Distance}}{\text{Speed}} = \dfrac{6}{15} = 0.4 \text{ hours}$

∴   Time in minutes = 0·4 × 60 = 24 minutes

Hence, the ship is closest to the lighthouse at noon + 24 minutes

= 12:24

Example

l is the line $x - 2y + 1 = 0$. The point $(3, k)$ is a distance $2\sqrt{5}$ from the line l. Find two possible values of k.

Solution

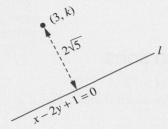

We have been given an equation in disguise, so using the formula:

$$\frac{|ax_1 + by_1 + c|}{\sqrt{a^2 + b^2}} = d$$

$$\frac{|1(3) - 2(k) + 1|}{\sqrt{1^2 + (-2)^2}} = 2\sqrt{5}$$

$$\frac{|4 - 2k|}{\sqrt{5}} = 2\sqrt{5}$$

$$|4 - 2k| = 2(5) = 10$$

$4 - 2k = 10$ or	$4 - 2k = -10$
$-2k = 6$	$-2k = -14$
$k = -3$	$k = 7$

Thus, $k = -3$ or   7.

The slope of a line when given its equation

To find the slope of a line when given its equation, do the following.

Method 1:

Get y on its own, and the number in front of x is the slope.

Note: The number in front of x is called the **coefficient** of x.
The number on its own is called the y-**intercept**.

In short: write the line in the form $y = mx + c$.

$y = \quad mx \quad + \qquad\qquad c \quad$ (see booklet of formulae and tables page 18)
$\qquad\quad \downarrow \qquad\qquad\qquad\quad \downarrow$

$y = (\text{slope})x + (\text{where the line cuts the } y\text{-axis})$

Method 2:

> If the line is in the form $ax + by + c = 0$, then $-\dfrac{a}{b}$ is the slope.

In other words: $\text{Slope} = -\dfrac{\text{Number in front of } x}{\text{Number in front of } y}$

key point

When using this method, make sure every term is on the left-hand side in the given equation of the line.

Angle between two lines

If two lines, l_1 and l_2, have slopes m_1 and m_2 respectively, and θ is the angle between them, then:

$$\tan \theta = \pm \frac{m_1 - m_2}{1 + m_1 m_2}$$ (see booklet of formulae and tables page 19)

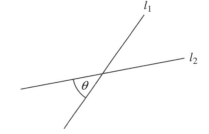

key point

If $\tan \theta$ is positive $\Rightarrow$ smaller angle = acute angle
If $\tan \theta$ is negative $\Rightarrow$ larger angle = obtuse angle

Example

Find the larger angle between the lines $2x + y + 5 = 0$ and $3x - 4y + 1 = 0$, in degrees correct to one decimal place.

Solution

$2x + y + 5 = 0 \Rightarrow y = -2x + 5 \Rightarrow m_1 = -2$

$3x - 4y + 1 = 0 \Rightarrow y = \frac{3}{4}x + \frac{1}{4} \Rightarrow m_2 = \frac{3}{4}$

Use $\tan \theta = \pm \dfrac{m_1 - m_2}{1 + m_1 m_2}$

$\tan \theta = \left| \dfrac{m_1 - m_2}{1 + m_1 m_2} \right| = \left| \dfrac{-2 - \frac{3}{4}}{1 + (-2)\left(\frac{3}{4}\right)} \right|$

$= \left| \dfrac{-\frac{11}{4}}{1 - \frac{3}{2}} \right| = \dfrac{11}{2}$

$\theta = \tan^{-1}\dfrac{11}{2} = 79.7°$

The larger angle $= 180° - 79.7° = 100.3°$

Find the slopes and the equations of the two lines that pass through the point (6, 1) and make an angle of $\theta = \tan^{-1}(1)$ with the line $x + 2y = 0$.

Solution

We will use the angle between two lines to find the slope(s) of the unknown line(s). Of the three values in this formula (m_1, m_2 and θ), we know the last two.

$$\tan \theta = \tan (\tan^{-1}(1)) = 1$$

Let the slope of the unknown line(s) be m. We expect to get two values for this. The slope of the given line must be found by rearranging its equation.

$x + 2y = 0$

$2y = x$

$y = -\dfrac{1}{2}x$

$\therefore \quad m_2 = -\dfrac{1}{2}$

$\tan \theta = \pm \dfrac{m_1 - m_2}{1 + m_1 m_2}$

$1 = \pm \dfrac{m - \left(-\frac{1}{2}\right)}{1 + m\left(-\frac{1}{2}\right)}$ (multiply each term on the RHS by 2)

$1 = \pm \dfrac{2m + 1}{2 - m}$

$$1 = \frac{2m + 1}{2 - m}$$

$$2 - m = 2m + 1$$

$$-3m = -1$$

$$m = \frac{1}{3}$$

$$1 = -\frac{2m + 1}{2 - m}$$

$$2 - m = -2m - 1$$

$$m = -3$$

The equations of the lines:

$$y - y_1 = m(x - x_1)$$

$$y - 1 = \frac{1}{3}(x - 6)$$

$$3y - 3 = x - 6$$

$$x - 3y - 3 = 0$$

$$y - y_1 = m(x - x_1)$$

$$y - 1 = -3(x - 6)$$

$$y - 1 = -3x + 18$$

$$3x + y - 19 = 0$$

(i) Show that the point $(1, 5)$ is on the line $2x - 5y + 23 = 0$.

(ii) If $2x - 5y + 23 = 0$, express y in terms of x.

(iii) A triangle ABC lies entirely in the first quadrant and has an area of $4\frac{1}{2}$ square units. The equation of one side of the triangle is $2x - 5y + 23 = 0$ and the vertices of A and B are $(1, 5)$ and $(3, 4)$, respectively. Find the coordinates of C.

Solution

(i) $2x - 5y + 23 = 2(1) - 5(5) + 23 = 2 - 25 + 23 = 0$
∴ $(1, 5)$ is on the line $2x - 5y + 23 = 0$.

(ii) Rearrange the equation of the line:

$$2x - 5y + 23 = 0$$

$$-5y = -2x - 23$$

$$y = \frac{2}{5}x + \frac{23}{5} \text{ or } \frac{2x + 23}{5}$$

(iii) As $B(3, 4)$ is not on $2x - 5y + 23 = 0$ (because $2(3) - 5(4) + 23 \neq 0$), we can deduce that C must be on it. From **(ii)**, we can describe C as $\left(x, \frac{2}{5}x + \frac{23}{5}\right)$. We need to move (translate) the points so that one of them is at the origin $(0, 0)$.

$$A(1, 5) \quad B(3, 4) \quad C\left(x, \frac{2}{5}x + \frac{23}{5}\right)$$

$$\downarrow \qquad \downarrow \qquad \qquad \downarrow$$

$$(0, 0) \quad (2, -1) \quad \left(x - 1, \frac{2}{5}x + \frac{23}{5} - 5\right)$$

$$= \left(x - 1, \frac{2}{5}x - \frac{2}{5}\right)$$

Area of triangle: $\dfrac{1}{2}\,|x_1\,y_2 - x_2\,y_1| = 4\dfrac{1}{2}$

$$\dfrac{1}{2}\left|(2)\left(\dfrac{2}{5}x - \dfrac{2}{5}\right) - (x-1)(-1)\right| = \dfrac{9}{2}$$

$$\left|(2)\left(\dfrac{2}{5}x - \dfrac{2}{5}\right) - (x-1)(-1)\right| = 9 \quad \text{(multiply both sides by 2)}$$

$$\left|\dfrac{4}{5}x - \dfrac{4}{5} + x - 1\right| = 9$$

$$\left|\dfrac{9}{5}x - \dfrac{9}{5}\right| = 9$$

$$|9x - 9| = 45 \quad \text{(multiply both sides by 5)}$$

$$|x - 1| = 5 \quad \text{(divide both sides by 9)}$$

$$x - 1 = 5 \qquad \text{or} \qquad x - 1 = -5$$
$$x = 6 \qquad\qquad\qquad x = -4$$

$$y = \dfrac{2x + 23}{5} \qquad\qquad \text{Reject}$$

$$= \dfrac{2(6) + 23}{5}$$

$$= \dfrac{35}{5}$$

$$= 7$$

As C must lie inside the first quadrant,

we reject $x = -4$. $\quad\therefore$ C is (6, 7).

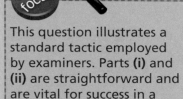

exam focus

This question illustrates a standard tactic employed by examiners. Parts **(i)** and **(ii)** are straightforward and are vital for success in a very challenging part **(iii)**.

---

exam Q

In the coordinate diagram shown, j, k and l are parallel lines. m and n are two more parallel lines.

The equations of four of the five lines are given in the table.

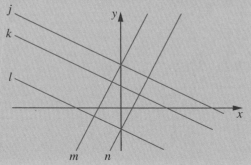

Equation	Line
$x + 2y = -4$	
$2x - y = -4$	
$x + 2y = 8$	
$2x - y = 2$	

(i) Complete the table by matching four of the lines to their equations.

(ii) Hence, insert scales on the x-axis and y-axis.

(iii) Hence, find the equation of the remaining line, given that its x-intercept and y-intercept are both integers.

Solution

(i) From the diagram, we know the lines j, k and l have a negative slope while m and n have a positive slope. We also note that j and m have the same positive y-intercept. Similarly, l and n share a negative y-intercept.

Rearrange the given equations into the form $y = mx + c$ and use the y-intercept (c) to identify the line uniquely.

Equation	y = mx + c	Might be	c	Line
$x + 2y = -4$	$y = -\frac{1}{2}x - 2$	j, k, l	-2	l
$2x - y = -4$	$y = 2x + 4$	m, n	$+4$	m
$x + 2y = 8$	$y = -\frac{1}{2}x + 4$	j, k, l	$+4$	j
$2x - y = 2$	$y = 2x - 2$	m, n	-2	n

(ii) We know the scale on the y-axis from the y-intercepts. To find the scale on the x-axis, we find some x-intercepts. It is possible to deduce the scale without calculating all of them.

Line	When y = 0	Point on x-axis
$j : x + 2y = 8$	$x = 8$	$(8, 0)$
$l : x + 2y = -4$	$x = -4$	$(-4, 0)$
$m : 2x - y = -4$	$x = -2$	$(-2, 0)$
$n : 2x - y = 2$	$x = 1$	$(1, 0)$

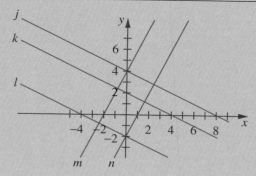

(iii) As k is parallel to j and l, its equation is of the form $x + 2y = t$. If t is not an even integer, the x-intercept or y-intercept (or both) will not be an integer. t must be below 8 (the line j) and above 0 (k does not pass through the origin).

As the original diagram suggests that k lies approximately halfway between the origin and the line j, its equation is most likely to be $x + 2y = 4$.

exam focus

This is a typical exam question. The candidate is required to absorb and process a large amount of information. The solution is simple and straightforward. Calmness and clarity of thought under exam pressure are essential for success in such questions.

2 Coordinate Geometry of the Circle

aims
- ☐ To know where to find the given coordinate geometry formulae in the booklet of formulae and tables
- ☐ To learn how to apply these formulae to procedural and in-context examination questions
- ☐ To know and apply the necessary formulae that are not in the booklet of formulae and tables
- ☐ To gain the ability, with practice, to recall relevant techniques and tactics necessary to succeed in the exam

Definitions

A circle is a set of points (a locus), each of which is equidistant from a fixed point called the **centre**.

The distance from the centre to any point on the circle is called the **radius**.

The formulae

Circle with centre (0, 0)

Two quantities are needed to find the equation of such a circle:

> **1.** Centre   **2.** Radius
>
> If the centre is (0, 0), the equation of the circle will be of the form $x^2 + y^2 = r^2$.

Circle with centre (h, k)

Two quantities are needed to find the equation of such a circle:

> **1.** Centre, (h, k) **2.** Radius, r
>
> Then use the formula $(x - h)^2 + (y - k)^2 = r^2$.

(see formulae and tables page 19)

The general equation of a circle is written as:

$$x^2 + y^2 + 2gx + 2fy + c = 0$$

(see formulae and tables page 19)

When the equation of a circle is given in this form, we use the following method to find its centre and radius.

1. Make sure every term is on the left-hand side and the coefficients of x^2 and y^2 are equal to 1.
2. Centre $= (-g, -f) = (-\frac{1}{2}$ coefficient of x, $-\frac{1}{2}$ coefficient of $y)$
3. Radius $= \sqrt{g^2 + f^2 - c}$ (provided $g^2 + f^2 - c > 0$)

key point

When we talk about the 'equation of a circle' we should really say 'the equation of the circumference of the circle'.

Points inside, on or outside a circle
Method 1

To find whether a point is inside, on or outside a circle, calculate the distance from the centre to the point and compare this distance with the radius. Three cases arise:

Inside	On	Outside
Distance from the centre to the point is **less** than the radius.	Distance from the centre to the point is **equal** to the radius.	Distance from the centre to the point is **greater** than the radius.
∴ Point is inside the circle.	∴ Point is on the circle.	∴ Point is outside the circle.

Method 2

The equation of a circle can be of the form:

$$x^2 + y^2 = r^2$$
$$(x - h)^2 + (y - k)^2 = r^2$$
$$x^2 + y^2 + 2gx + 2fy + c = 0$$

If the coordinates of a point satisfy the equation of a circle, then the point is **on** the circle. Otherwise, the point is either **inside** or **outside** the circle. By substituting the coordinates into the equation of the circle, one of the following situations can arise:

1. LHS < RHS: the point is **inside** the circle.
2. LHS = RHS: the point is **on** the circle.
3. LHS > RHS: the point is **outside** the circle.

Remember the difference between a **circle** and a **disc**. A circle is similar to a ring while a disc is similar to a dinner plate. Therefore, a disc contains all the points on the edge **and** those within that boundary. A circle would refer only to those edge points.

The phrase 'The circle contains the point *P*' means that *P* is **on** the circumference of the circle rather than being a point enclosed by it.

Intersection of a line and a circle

To find the points where a line and a circle meet, the **method of substitution** between their equations is used.

The method involves the following three steps:

1. Get *x* or *y* on its own from the equation of the line.
   (Look carefully and select the variable which will make the work easier.)
2. Substitute for this same variable into the equation of the circle and solve the resultant quadratic equation.
3. Substitute **separately** the value(s) obtained in step 2 into the linear equation in step 1 to find the corresponding value(s) of the other variable.

If there is only **one point of intersection** between a line and a circle, then the line is a **tangent** to the circle.

Finding the equation of a circle

If the centre and radius are given, or can be found, then using the formula

$$(x-h)^2 + (y-k)^2 = r^2$$

is the preferred method for finding the equation of a circle.

However, for many questions it is difficult to find the centre and radius.

In these questions we have to use an algebraic approach or rely on our knowledge of the geometry of a circle to find the centre and radius.

Note: In some questions we can only use an algebraic approach.

In using an algebraic approach, we let the circle be $x^2 + y^2 + 2gx + 2fy + c = 0$ and use the information in the question to find g, f and c.

Given three points P, Q and R on the circle

Method 1: Algebraic approach

Let the equation of the circle be $x^2 + y^2 + 2gx + 2fy + c = 0$.

1. Substitute each point into this equation.
2. This gives three equations in three unknowns: g, f and c.
3. Solve these equations for g, f and c.
4. Put these values back into the equation.

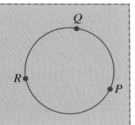

Method 2: Geometric approach

1. Find the equations of the perpendicular bisectors b_1 and b_2 of the chords $[PQ]$ and $[QR]$, respectively.
   (The perpendicular bisector of a chord passes through the centre.)
2. The centre of the circle is the point of intersection of b_1 and b_2 ($b_1 \cap b_2 = \{C\}$).
   (Solve the equations of b_1 and b_2 simultaneously.)
3. The radius is the distance from C to P, Q or R.
4. Use the formula: $(x - h)^2 + (y - k)^2 = r^2$.

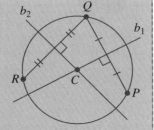

key point

There is only one circle that contains the points P, Q and R.

Given two points *P* and *Q* on the circle and the equation of a line, *l*, containing the centre *C*(−*g*,−*f*)

Method 1: Algebraic approach

> Let the equation of the circle be $x^2 + y^2 + 2gx + 2fy + c = 0$.
> 1. Substitute each point into this equation.
> 2. Substitute $(-g, -f)$ into the equation of the given line, *l*.
> 3. This gives three equations in three unknowns: *g*, *f* and *c*.
> 4. Solve these equations for *g*, *f* and *c*.
> 5. Put these values back into the equation.

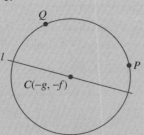

Method 2: Geometric approach

> 1. Find the equation of *b*, the perpendicular bisector of [*PQ*].
> 2. Solve the simultaneous equations *l* and *b* to find the centre.
> 3. Find the radius, *r*, the distance from the centre, *C*, to *P* or *Q*.
> 4. Use the formula $(x - h)^2 + (y - k)^2 = r^2$.

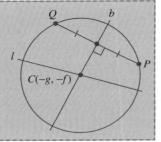

key point

> A line perpendicular to a tangent at the point of tangency passes through (contains) the centre of the circle.

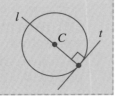

Given two points, *P* and *Q*, on the circle and the equation of the tangent at one of these points

Method

> 1. Find the equation of *l*, the line perpendicular to the tangent, *t*, passing through the given point of contact. This line will contain the centre, *C*.
> 2. Now we have two points on the circumference of the circle and the equation of a line that contains the centre of the circle.
> 3. Use an algebraic approach or use a geometric approach.

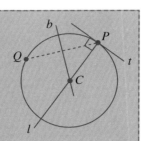

Circles with the axes as tangents

If a circle touches an axis (the x- or y-axis is a tangent to the circle), then one of the coordinates of the centre of the circle is equal to the radius.

1. Circle touching the x-axis

$$\text{Radius } = |-f|$$
$$\sqrt{g^2 + f^2 - c} = |-f|$$
$$g^2 + f^2 - c = f^2$$
$$g^2 - c = 0$$
$$g^2 = c$$

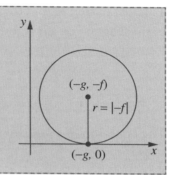

2. Circle touching the y-axis

$$\text{Radius } = |-g|$$
$$\sqrt{g^2 + f^2 - c} = |-g|$$
$$g^2 + f^2 - c = g^2$$
$$f^2 - c = 0$$
$$f^2 = c$$

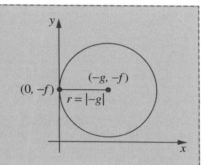

key point

- If the circle touches both the x- and y-axes, then $g^2 = f^2 = c$.
- If the centre is in the 1st or 3rd quadrant, its centre will lie on the line $y = x$.
- If the centre is in the 2nd or 4th quadrant, its centre will lie on the line $y = -x$.

Circles intersecting the axes

To find where a circle intersects the axes, we use the following.

The circle intersects the x-axis at $y = 0$.
The circle intersects the y-axis at $x = 0$.

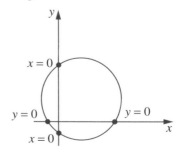

Equation of a tangent to a circle at a given point

A tangent is perpendicular to the radius that joins the centre
of a circle to the point of tangency.

This fact is used to find the slope of the tangent.

In the diagram on the right, the radius, r, is perpendicular to
the tangent, t, at the point of tangency, P.

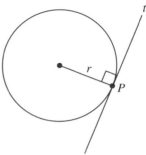

**The equation of a tangent to a circle at a given point is found with the following
steps.**

> 1. Find the slope of the radius to the point of tangency.
> 2. Turn this slope upside down and change its sign. This gives the slope of the tangent.
> 3. Use the coordinates of the point of contact and the slope of the tangent at this point in the formula:
>
> $$(y - y_1) = m(x - x_1)$$
>
> This gives the equation of the tangent.

key point

A diagram is often very useful.

Length of a tangent to a circle from a point outside the circle

The **length of a tangent** from a point outside a circle is the
distance, d, from the point outside the circle to the point of
tangency.

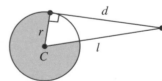

> 1. Find the centre, C, and radius length, r, of the circle.
> 2. Find the distance, l, between the centre and the point outside the circle.
> 3. Use Pythagoras' theorem to find d, i.e. $l^2 = r^2 + d^2$.

Radius perpendicular to a chord

A radius (or part of a radius) that is perpendicular to a chord bisects that chord. This also enables us to use Pythagoras' theorem:

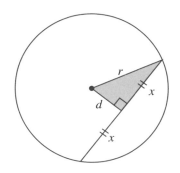

$$d^2 + x^2 = r^2$$

Thus, knowing two of d, x and r, we can find the third.

Equations of tangents from a point outside a circle

From a point outside a circle, two tangents can be drawn to touch the circle.

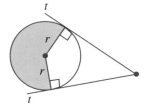

Method for finding the two equations of tangents from a point (x_1, y_1) outside a circle:

1. Find the centre and radius length of the circle (a rough diagram can help).
2. Let the equation be $y - y_1 = m(x - x_1)$ and write the equation in the form $ax + by + c = 0$.
3. Let the perpendicular distance from the centre of the circle to the tangent equal the radius.
4. Solve this equation to find two values of m.
5. Using these two values of m and the point (x_1, y_1), write down the equations of the two tangents.

Touching circles

Two circles are said to be **touching** if they have only one point of intersection. To investigate whether two circles touch, we compare the distance between their centres with the sum or difference of their radii.

Consider two circles of radius r_1 and r_2 (where $r_1 > r_2$) and let d be the distance between their centres.

1. Circles touch externally

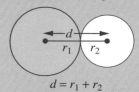

$$d = r_1 + r_2$$

Distance between their centres
= sum of their radii

2. Circles touch internally

$$d = r_1 - r_2$$

Distance between their centres
= difference of their radii

Common chord or common tangent

If $s_1 = 0$ and $s_2 = 0$ are the equations of two circles in standard form, then $s_1 - s_2 = 0$ is the equation of the common chord or common tangent of the two circles.

Common chord

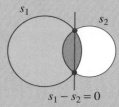

$$s_1 - s_2 = 0$$

Two points of intersection

Common tangent

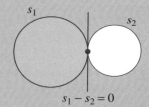

$$s_1 - s_2 = 0$$

One point of intersection

key point

To find the equation of the common chord, or common tangent, of two circles, $s_1 = 0$ and $s_2 = 0$, the coefficients of x^2 and y^2 must be the same for both circles.

To find the coordinates of the points of intersection of two circles, do the following.

1. Find the equation of the common chord ($s_1 - s_2 = 0$).
2. Solve between the equation of the common chord and the equation of one of the circles.

Example

Find the centre and radius of the following circles.

(i) $x^2 + y^2 = 9$ (ii) $(x - 2)^2 + (x + 3)^2 = 20$

(iii) $(x + 7)(x + 3) + (y - 2)(y + 2) = 0$

Solution

(i) $x^2 + y^2 = 9$ (ii) $(x - 2)^2 + (y + 3)^2 = 20$

Centre $= (0, 0)$ and radius $= 3$ Centre $= (2, -3)$ and radius $= \sqrt{20}$

(iii) $(x + 7)(x + 3) + (y - 2)(y + 2) = 0$

First write the equation in the form $x^2 + y^2 + 2gx + 2fy + c = 0$.

$$(x + 7)(x + 3) + (y - 2)(y + 2) = 0$$
$$x^2 + 10x + 21 + y^2 - 4 = 0$$
$$x^2 + y^2 + 10x + 0y + 17 = 0$$

Centre $= (-g, -f) = (-5, 0)$

Radius $= \sqrt{g^2 + f^2 - c} = \sqrt{(-5)^2 + (0)^2 - 17} = \sqrt{8}$

A circle with centre $(-3, 7)$ passes through the point $(5, -8)$. Find the equation of the circle.

Solution

We have the centre and require the radius.

Radius $r =$ distance between the points $(-3, 7)$ and $(5, -8)$.

$$r = \sqrt{(5 + 3)^2 + (-8 - 7)^2}$$
$$= \sqrt{8^2 + (-15)^2} = \sqrt{64 + 225} = \sqrt{289} = 17$$

Equation of the circle: $(x - h)^2 + (y - k)^2 = r^2$
$$(x + 3)^2 + (y - 7)^2 = 17^2$$
$$x^2 + 6x + 9 + y^2 - 14y + 49 = 289$$
$$x^2 + y^2 + 6x - 14y - 231 = 0$$

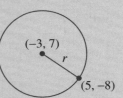

The starting point for the majority of exam questions on the circle will involve either one of the previous two examples. You must be totally familiar with both exam techniques.

Example

Find the equation of the tangent to the circle $x^2 + y^2 - 4x - 8y - 5 = 0$ at the point $(6, 7)$ on the circle.

Solution

Method 1

Centre of the circle $= (-g, -f) = (2, 4)$

Slope of the radius, r, from $(2, 4)$ to the point $(6, 7)$

$$= m = \frac{y_2 - y_1}{x_2 - x_1} = \frac{7 - 4}{6 - 2} = \frac{3}{4}$$

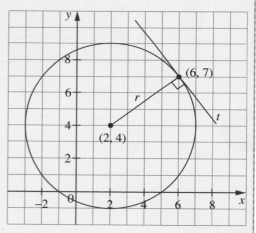

$\therefore$ The slope of the tangent at $(6, 7)$ is $-\frac{4}{3}$.

Equation of the tangent, t:

$$(y - y_1) = m(x - x_1)$$

$$(y - 7) = -\frac{4}{3}(x - 6)$$

$$3y - 21 = -4x + 24$$

$$4x + 3y - 45 = 0$$

Method 2

Equation of tangent given by $xx_1 + yy_1 + g(x + x_1) + f(y + y_1) + c = 0$
(see formulae and tables page 19)

$$\left. \begin{array}{l} x_1 = 6 \\ y_1 = 7 \\ g = -2 \\ f = -4 \\ c = -5 \end{array} \right\}$$
$$6x + 7y - 2(x + 6) - 4(y + 7) - 5 = 0$$
$$6x + 7y - 2x - 12 - 4y - 28 - 5 = 0$$
$$4x + 3y - 45 = 0$$

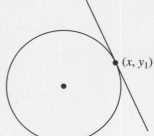

In many circle questions it will be very worthwhile to draw a sketch of the situation. The sketch can help you focus on what is given and what is required.

Example

$x^2 + y^2 - 6x + 4y - 12 = 0$ is the equation of a circle, c.
Determine whether each of the points $(7, -3)$, $(-1, -5)$ and $(9, 2)$ is inside, on or outside c.

Solution

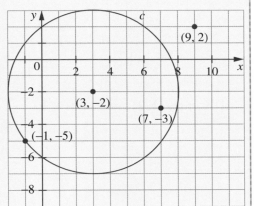

$$x^2 + y^2 - 6x + 4y - 12$$

$(7, -3)$: $7^2 + (-3)^2 - 6(7) + 4(-3) - 12$
$= -8 < 0 \therefore (7, -3)$ is inside c.

$(-1, -5)$: $(-1)^2 + (-5)^2 - 6(-1)$
$+ 4(-5) - 12$
$= 0 \therefore (-1, -5)$ is on c.

$(9, 2)$: $(9)^2 + (2)^2 - 6(9) + 4(2) - 12$
$= 27 > 0 \therefore (9, 2)$ is outside c.

Example

$A(3, 5)$ and $B(-1, -1)$ are the end points of a diameter of a circle, s.
  (i) Find the centre and radius length of s.
 (ii) Find the equation of s.
(iii) s intersects the x-axis at P and Q, $P < Q$. Find the coordinates of P and Q.

Solution

(i) Centre is the midpoint of $[AB]$.
    $A(3, 5)$ $B(-1, -1)$

  The midpoint of $[AB] = \left(\dfrac{3 - 1}{2}, \dfrac{5 - 1}{2} \right) = (1, 2)$.

  The radius is the distance from $(1, 2)$ to $(3, 5)$ or $(-1, -1)$.

  Thus, the radius $= \sqrt{(3 - 1)^2 + (5 - 2)^2} = \sqrt{2^2 + 3^2} = \sqrt{13}$.

  Centre $= (1, 2)$ and radius $= \sqrt{13}$

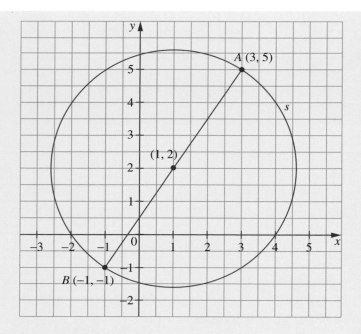

(ii) Centre $(1, 2)$ and radius $\sqrt{13}$

$$(x - h)^2 + (y - k)^2 = r^2$$
$$(x - 1)^2 + (y - 2)^2 = (\sqrt{13})^2$$
$$x^2 - 2x + 1 + y^2 - 4y + 4 = 13$$
$$x^2 + y^2 - 2x - 4y - 8 = 0$$

(iii) On the x-axis, $y = 0$.

$$x^2 + y^2 - 2x - 4y - 8 = 0$$
$$x^2 + 0^2 - 2x - 4(0) - 8 = 0$$
$$x^2 - 2x - 8 = 0$$
$$(x + 2)(x - 4) = 0$$
$$x = -2 \text{ or } x = 4$$

Thus, s intersects the x-axis at $P(-2, 0)$ and $Q(4, 0)$.

Example

(i) Show that for all values of $t \in \mathbb{R}$, the point $\left(\dfrac{2t}{1+t^2}, \dfrac{1-t^2}{1+t^2}\right)$ lies on the circle $x^2 + y^2 = 1$.

(ii) By selecting a value for t, where $t \in \mathbb{R}$, verify your answer for that value of t.

Solution

(i)
$$x^2 + y^2 = \left(\frac{2t}{1+t^2}\right)^2 + \left(\frac{1-t^2}{1+t^2}\right)^2$$

$$= \frac{4t^2}{1+2t^2+t^4} + \frac{1-2t^2+t^4}{1+2t^2+t^4}$$

$$= \frac{4t^2+1-2t^2+t^4}{1+2t^2+t^4} = \frac{1+2t^2+t^4}{1+2t^2+t^4} = 1$$

(ii) Let $t = 2$ (or any real number).

$$x^2 + y^2 = \left(\frac{2(2)}{1+(2)^2}\right)^2 + \left(\frac{1-(2)^2}{1+(2)^2}\right)^2$$

$$= \left(\frac{4}{5}\right)^2 + \left(-\frac{3}{5}\right)^2 = \frac{16}{25} + \frac{9}{25} = \frac{25}{25} = 1$$

exam focus

The above type of question often causes problems for candidates. As usual in these questions, the successful solution is routine. Simply replace x with the first ordinate $\dfrac{2t}{1+t^2}$ and replace y with the second ordinate $\dfrac{1-t^2}{1+t^2}$.

The points $A(-2, 4)$, $B(0, -10)$ and $C(6, -2)$ are the coordinates of the vertices of triangle ABC.

(i) Verify that the triangle is right-angled at C.

(ii) Hence or otherwise, find the equation of the circumcircle of triangle ABC.

Solution

(i) Draw a diagram.

Slope of $AC = m_1 = \dfrac{-2 - 4}{6 + 2} = \dfrac{-6}{8} = -\dfrac{3}{4}$

Slope of $BC = m_2 = \dfrac{-2 + 10}{6 - 0} = \dfrac{8}{6} = \dfrac{4}{3}$

$m_1 \times m_2 = -\dfrac{3}{4} \times \dfrac{4}{3} = -1$

$\therefore \quad AC \perp BC$

$\therefore \quad$ Triangle is right-angled at C.

(ii) $[AB]$ is the diameter of the circumcircle, as triangle ABC is right-angled at C. The midpoint, P, of $[AB]$ is the centre of the circumcircle.

The coordinates of the centre $P = \left(\dfrac{-2 - 0}{2}, \dfrac{4 - 10}{2}\right) = \left(\dfrac{-2}{2}, \dfrac{-6}{2}\right) = (-1, -3)$

Radius $= |PA|$ or $|PB|$ or $|PC|$.

Radius $= |PA| = \sqrt{(-1 + 2)^2 + (-3 - 4)^2} = \sqrt{(1)^2 + (-7)^2}$

$\qquad = \sqrt{1 + 49} = \sqrt{50}$

We have the centre $= (-1, -3) = (h, k)$ and the radius $= \sqrt{50} = r$.

$(x - h)^2 + (y - k)^2 = r^2$

$(x + 1)^2 + (y + 3)^2 = (\sqrt{50})^2$

$(x + 1)^2 + (y + 3)^2 = 50$

$\qquad$ or

$x^2 + y^2 + 2x + 6y - 40 = 0$

(Diagram: circle through $A(-2, 4)$, $C(6, -2)$, $B(0, -10)$ with triangle ABC right-angled at C.)

From a theorem in geometry you should know that the angle in a semicircle is right-angled. Hence in this case $[AB]$ is a diameter of the required circle. This is yet another case of course content overlap: coordinate geometry with Euclidean geometry.

Find the values of $k \in \mathbb{R}$ for which the line $x - y + k = 0$ is a tangent to the circle $(x - 3)^2 + (y + 4)^2 = 50$.

Solution

$(x - 3)^2 + (y + 4)^2 = 50$

Centre $= (3, -4)$ and radius $= \sqrt{50}$

$x - y + k = 0$ is a tangent to the circle.

∴ The distance from the centre $(3, -4)$ to the line $x - y + k = 0$ must equal the radius.

$$\frac{|ax_1 + by_1 + c|}{\sqrt{a^2 + b^2}} = d$$

$$\frac{|1(3) - 1(-4) + k|}{\sqrt{1^2 + (-1)^2}} = \sqrt{50}$$

$$\frac{|k + 7|}{\sqrt{2}} = 5\sqrt{2} \qquad \text{(multiply both sides by } \sqrt{2}\text{)}$$

$$|k + 7| = 10$$

$$k + 7 = 10 \qquad \text{or} \qquad k + 7 = -10$$

$$k = 3 \qquad \text{or} \qquad k = -17$$

(In figure: $x - y + k = 0$, $\sqrt{50}$, $(3, -4)$, $x - y + k = 0$)

The perpendicular distance from the centre of a circle to the tangent is always equal to the radius.

To develop the above exam question, it could ask, for example, to describe the relationship between the given circle $(x - 3)^2 + (y + 4)^2 = 50$ and the system of lines $x - y + k = 0$ when $-17 < k < 3$, $x \in \mathbb{R}$.

Answer using the previous solution.

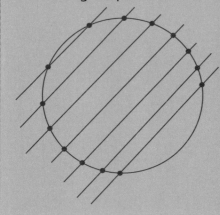

The lines are all parallel to each other and each line intersects the circle twice.

This type of 'what if' testing will be a common feature at the end of procedural exam questions. It will be useful for candidates to know this and develop strategies to cope with such features.

Example

The point $A(5, 2)$ is on the circle $c: x^2 + y^2 + px - 2y + 5 = 0$.

(i) Find the value of p.

(ii) The line $l: x - y - 1 = 0$ intersects the circle c. Find the coordinates of the points of intersection.

Solution

(i) $A(5, 2)$ is on the circle $x^2 + y^2 + px - 2y + 5 = 0$.

$$\therefore \quad (5)^2 + (2)^2 + p(5) - 2(2) + 5 = 0$$
$$25 + 4 + 5p - 4 + 5 = 0$$
$$5p + 30 = 0$$
$$5p = -30$$
$$p = -6$$

(ii) Intersection of the line l: $x - y - 1 = 0$ and the circle c:

$$x^2 + y^2 - 6x - 2y + 5 = 0$$
$$x - y - 1 = 0$$
$$x = y + 1 \qquad \text{(x on its own)}$$
$$x^2 + y^2 - 6x - 2y + 5 = 0$$
$$(y + 1)^2 + y^2 - 6(y + 1) - 2y + 5 = 0 \qquad \text{(put in $(y + 1)$ for x)}$$
$$y^2 + 2y + 1 + y^2 - 6y - 6 - 2y + 5 = 0$$
$$2y^2 - 6y = 0$$
$$y^2 - 3y = 0$$
$$y(y - 3) = 0$$
$$y = 0 \text{ or } y = 3$$

$x = y + 1$	
$y = 0$	$y = 3$
$x = 0 + 1$	$x = 3 + 1$
$x = 1$	$x = 4$
$(1, 0)$	$(4, 3)$

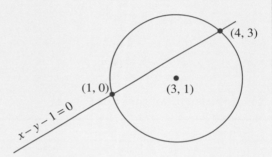

Many circle problems where chords are mentioned are easily solved by drawing a sketch and reviewing the information given. In particular, you should remember that a chord is bisected by a diameter, or radius, perpendicular to the chord.

Example

The point $(4, 1)$ is the midpoint of a chord of the circle
$x^2 + y^2 - 6x + 2y - 15 = 0$.
Find the length of this chord.

Solution

The centre of the circle is $(3, -1)$.

Its radius length is $\sqrt{g^2 + f^2 - c} = \sqrt{(-3)^2 + 1^2 - (-15)} = 5$.

Draw a sketch.

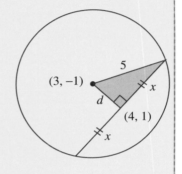

$$d = \sqrt{(x_2 - x_1)^2 + (y_2 - y_1)^2}$$
$$= \sqrt{(4 - 3)^2 + (1 - (-1))^2} = \sqrt{5}$$

Applying Pythagoras' theorem:

$$d^2 + x^2 = 5^2$$
$$(\sqrt{5})^2 + x^2 = 25$$
$$5 + x^2 = 25$$
$$x = \sqrt{20} = 2\sqrt{5}$$

Thus, the length of the chord $= 2x = 2(2\sqrt{5}) = 4\sqrt{5}$ units.

Drawing a diagram often turns a difficult-looking question into a simple, routine solution.

Example

s_1 and s_2 are two circles which touch externally.
The centre of s_1 is $(13, 3)$ and the equation of s_2 is $x^2 + y^2 - 2x + 4y - 11 = 0$.
Find the equation of:

(i) s_1 (ii) the common tangent, t, at the point of contact.

Solution

Draw a diagram.

(i) $s_2 : x^2 + y^2 - 2x + 4y - 11 = 0$

Centre of $s_2 = C_2 (1, -2)$ and radius of $s_2 = r_2$

$= \sqrt{1^2 + (-2)^2 - (-11)} = 4$

Distance between centres:

$|C_1 C_2| = \sqrt{(13 - 1)^2 + (3 + 2)^2} = 13$

As the circles touch externally:

$r_1 + r_2 = |C_1 C_2|$

$r_1 + 4 = 13$

$r_1 = 9$

Thus, the radius r_1 of s_1 is 9.

Equation of circle s_1:

$$(x - 13)^2 + (y - 3)^2 = 9^2$$
$$x^2 - 26x + 169 + y^2 - 6y + 9 = 81$$
$$x^2 + y^2 - 26x - 6y + 97 = 0$$

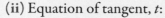

(ii) Equation of tangent, t:

$$s_1 - s_2 = 0$$
$$(x^2 + y^2 - 26x - 6y + 97) - (x^2 + y^2 - 2x + 4y - 11) = 0$$
$$-24x - 10y + 108 = 0$$
$$12x + 5y - 54 = 0$$

Example

Find the equations of the two tangents from the point $(6, -4)$ to the circle $x^2 + y^2 - 6x + 10y + 26 = 0$.

Solution

$x^2 + y^2 - 6x + 10y + 26 = 0$

Centre $= (-g, -f) = (3, -5)$

Radius $= \sqrt{g^2 + f^2 - c} = \sqrt{(3)^2 + (-5)^2 - 26} = \sqrt{8}$

We have a point $(6, -4)$ on both tangents.

We need the slopes of the two tangents.

Equation of the tangents (in terms of m):

$$(y + 4) = m(x - 6)$$
$$y + 4 = mx - 6m$$
$$mx - y + (-6m - 4) = 0$$

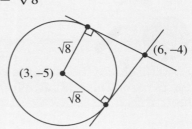

The distance from the centre of the circle, $(3, -5)$, to the line $mx - y + (-6m - 4) = 0$ is equal to the radius, $\sqrt{8}$.

$$\therefore \frac{|m(3) + (-1)(-5) + (-6m - 4)|}{\sqrt{m^2 + (-1)^2}} = \sqrt{8} \qquad \text{(perpendicular distance formula)}$$

$$\frac{|3m + 5 - 6m - 4|}{\sqrt{m^2 + 1}} = \sqrt{8}$$

$$\frac{|-3m + 1|}{\sqrt{m^2 + 1}} = \sqrt{8}$$

$$\frac{9m^2 - 6m + 1}{m^2 + 1} = 8 \qquad \text{(square both sides)}$$

$$9m^2 - 6m + 1 = 8m^2 + 8 \qquad \text{(multiply both sides by } (m^2 + 1))$$

$$m^2 - 6m - 7 = 0$$

$$(m + 1)(m - 7) = 0$$

$$m = -1 \quad \text{or} \quad m = 7$$

Equations of the two tangents

Slope $= -1$, point $= (6, -4)$

$$(y + 4) = -1(x - 6)$$
$$y + 4 = -x + 6$$
$$x + y - 2 = 0$$

Slope $= 7$, point $= (6, -4)$

$$(y + 4) = 7(x - 6)$$
$$y + 4 = 7x - 42$$
$$7x - y - 46 = 0$$

key point

When a question requires the equation of two circles that satisfy the same conditions, try to form a quadratic equation in g or f. For example, $g^2 - 2g - 8 = 0$, $f^2 - f - 6 = 0$.

exam focus

For difficult questions on the coordinate geometry of a circle, it is very common for the perpendicular distance formula to be a key component of a successful solution.

(i) The y-axis is a tangent to the circle
$x^2 + y^2 + 2gx + 2fy + c = 0$. Prove that $f^2 = c$.

(ii) Find the equations of the circles that pass through the points $(-3, 6)$ and $(-6, 3)$ and have the y-axis as a tangent.

Solution

(i) Already done in a previous section of this chapter.

(ii) Let the circle be $x^2 + y^2 + 2gx + 2fy + c = 0$.

Touches the y-axis, $\therefore$ $f^2 = c$.   ①

This equation contains f^2 so we should use this equation last and substitute into it. The points $(-3, 6)$ and $(-6, 3)$ are on the circle.

$\therefore$ $(-3)^2 + (6)^2 + 2g(-3)$ $(-6)^2 + (3)^2 + 2g(-6)$

$+ 2f(6) + c = 0$ $+ 2f(3) + c = 0$

$9 + 36 - 6g + 12f + c = 0$ $36 + 9 - 12g + 6f + c = 0$

$-6g + 12f + c = -45$ $-12g + 6f + c = -45$

$6g - 12f - c = 45$ ② $12g - 6f - c = 45$ ③

There is no g in the equation $f^2 = c$. ①

Thus, we eliminate g using equations ② and ③.

$12g - 24f - 2c = 90$ ② × 2	$f^2 = c$ ①
$-12g + 6f + c = -45$ ③ × −1	$f^2 = -18f - 45$
$\overline{-18f - c = 45}$	$f^2 + 18f + 45 = 0$
$-c = 18f + 45$	$(f + 3)(f + 15) = 0$
$c = -18f - 45$	$f = -3$ or $f = -15$

(Put this into equation ①.)

Case 1	Case 2
$f = -3$	$f = -15$
$c = f^2 = (-3)^2 = 9$	$c = f^2 = (-15)^2 = 225$
$6g - 12f - c = 45$ ②	$6g - 12f - c = 45$ ②
$6g - 12(-3) - 9 = 45$	$6g - 12(-15) - 225 = 45$
$6g + 36 - 9 = 45$	$6g + 180 - 225 = 45$
$6g = 18$	$6g = 90$
$g = 3$	$g = 15$
$x^2 + y^2 + 2(3)x + 2(-3)y + 9 = 0$	$x^2 + y^2 + 2(15)x + 2(-15)y + 225 = 0$
$x^2 + y^2 + 6x - 6y + 9 = 0$	$x^2 + y^2 + 30x - 30y + 225 = 0$

An earring is to be made from silver wire.

The design is two touching circles with two tangents to the larger circle, as shown in diagram 1.

Diagram 2 is a drawing of this earring imposed on the coordinated axes.

The equation of the inner circle is $x^2 + y^2 + 3y = 0.$

The outer circle intersects the y-axis at $(0, -4)$.

The tangents meet the y-axis at $(0, -6)$.

Find the total length of silver wire required to make this earring. Give your answer correct to the nearest integer.

Diagram 1

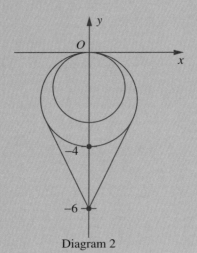

Diagram 2

Solution

We need to find the lengths of the circumferences of the inner and outer circles and the lengths of the two tangents.

Inner circle	**Outer circle**

Inner circle

$x^2 + y^2 + 3y = 0$

$\text{Centre} = (-g, -f) = \left(0, -\frac{3}{2}\right)$

$\therefore \text{Radius} = \frac{3}{2}$

$\text{Circumference} = 2\pi r = 2\pi\left(\frac{3}{2}\right) = 3\pi$

Outer circle

Centre = midpoint of $(0, 0)$ and $(0, -4)$

$= (0, -2)$

$\therefore \quad \text{Radius} = 2$

$\text{Circumference} = 2\pi r = 2\pi(2) = 4\pi$

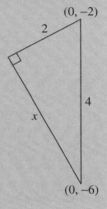

Lengths of the two tangents

Using Pythagoras' theorem:

$$x^2 + 2^2 = 4^2$$
$$x^2 + 4 = 16$$
$$x^2 = 12$$
$$x = \sqrt{12}$$

$\therefore \quad$ Length of the two tangents $= 2x = 2\sqrt{12}$.

Total length of silver wire required to make the earring

$$= 3\pi + 4\pi + 2\sqrt{12} = 29 \quad \text{(correct to the nearest integer)}$$

The diagram shows a penny-farthing bicycle supported on a stand at points *P* and *R* on the front wheel.

Each unit on the axes is 5 cm.

The equation of the rear wheel is $x^2 + y^2 - 6y = 0$.

The equation of the front wheel is $x^2 + y^2 - 28x - 20y + 196 = 0$.

(i) **(a)** Find the distance between the centres of the two wheels, correct to the nearest cm.

(b) Hence, calculate the clearence (smallest gap) between the front and rear wheels, correct to the nearest mm.

(ii) $Q(7, 3)$ is halfway between *P* and *R*, and *S* is the centre of the front wheel.

(a) Find the slope of *SQ*.

(b) Hence, find the equation of *PR* and the coordinates of *P* and *R*.

Solution

Rear wheel: $x^2 + y^2 - 6y = 0$

Centre $= (-g, -f) = (0, 3)$

Radius $= \sqrt{g^2 + f^2 - c}$

$\quad\ = \sqrt{0^2 + 3^2 - 0} = 3$

Front wheel: $x^2 + y^2 - 28x - 20y + 196 = 0$

Centre $= (-g, -f) = (14, 10)$

Radius $= \sqrt{g^2 + f^2 - c}$

$\quad\ = \sqrt{14^2 + 10^2 - 196}$

$\quad\ = \sqrt{100} = 10$

(i) (a) Distance between (0, 3) and (14, 10)

$|PS| = \sqrt{(14 - 0)^2 + (10 - 3)^2}$

$= \sqrt{14^2 + 7^2} = \sqrt{245}$

∴ Actual distance between centres

$= 5 \times \sqrt{245} = 78$ cm   (nearest cm)

(b) The clearance

= smallest gap

$= |PS| - 3 - 10$

$= \sqrt{245} - 13$

Actual clearance

$= 5(\sqrt{245} - 13)$

$= 13\cdot26237921$ cm

$= 133$ (nearest mm)

(ii) (a) $S(14, 10)$, $Q(7, 3)$

Slope of $SQ = \dfrac{3 - 10}{7 - 14} = \dfrac{-7}{-7} = 1$

∴ Slope of $PR = -1$ (Part of a radius that bisects a chord is perpendicular to that chord.)

(b) The equation of PR

Slope $= -1$, point $= Q = (7, 3)$

$(y - 3) = -(x - 7)$

$y - 3 = -x + 7$

$x + y - 10 = 0$

Now to find P and R

$y = 10 - x$ (y on its own)

$x^2 + y^2 - 28x - 20y + 196 = 0$

$x^2 + (10 - x)^2 - 28x - 20(10 - x) + 196 = 0$

$x^2 + 100 - 20x + x^2 - 28x - 200 + 20x + 196 = 0$

$2x^2 - 28x + 96 = 0$

$x^2 - 14x + 48 = 0$

$(x - 6)(x - 8) = 0$

$x = 6$ or $x = 8$

$y = 10 - x$	
$x = 6$	$x = 8$
$y = 10 - 6$	$y = 10 - 8$
$x = 4$	$y = 2$
$P (6, 4)$	$R (8, 2)$

aims

- [ ] To know the definitions of the geometry terms listed in the glossary
- [ ] To know all theorems, corollaries and axioms
- [ ] To be able to reproduce the proofs for theorems 11, 12 and 13
- [ ] To be able to solve problems by applying the theorems, corollaries and axioms

GLOSSARY OF EXAMINABLE TERMS

Axiom: A statement which is assumed to be true. It can be accepted without a proof and used as a basis for an argument.

Converse: The converse of a theorem is formed by taking the conclusion as the starting point and having the starting point as the conclusion.

Corollary: A corollary follows after a theorem and is a statement which must be true because of that theorem.

If and only if: Often shortened to 'iff'. One statement is true if and only if the second statement is true, so both statements must be true or both statements must be false.

Implies: Implies indicates a logical relationship between two statements, such that if the first is true then the second must be true.

Is congruent to: Two things are said to be congruent if they are identical in size and shape.

Is equivalent to: Two things are said to be equivalent if they have the same value but different forms.

Proof: A sequence of statements (made up of axioms, assumptions and arguments) that follow logically from the preceding one, starting at an axiom or previously proven theorem and ending with the statement of the theorem to be proven.

Proof by contradiction: A proof which establishes the truth of a statement by proving that the statement being false leads to a contradiction. Proving its falsity to be impossible proves that the statement must be true.

Theorem: A statement which has been proven to be true, deduced from axioms by logical argument.

exam focus

You must learn these definitions and be able to reproduce them in the exam.

You are required to know the following axioms, theorems and corollaries and you must be able to apply them in answering geometric questions.

Axioms

Axiom 1: There is exactly one line through any two given points.

Axiom 2: **Ruler axiom**

The distance between points P and Q has the following properties:

1. The distance $|PQ|$ is never negative.
2. The distance between two points is the same whether we measure from P to Q or from Q to P.
3. If there exists some point R between P and Q, then the distance from P to Q is equal to the sum of the distances from P to R and R to Q.

$$|PR| + |RQ| = |PQ|$$

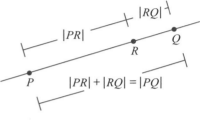

4. Marking off a distance
   Given any ray from P, and given any real number $k \geq 0$, there is a unique point Q on the ray whose distance from P is k.

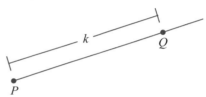

Axiom 3: **Protractor axiom**

The number of degrees in an angle (also known as its degree-measure) is always a number between $0°$ and $360°$.
It has these properties:

1. A straight angle has $180°$.
2. If we know the angle $A°$, opened up at a point P, then there are two possible rays from P that form that angle.

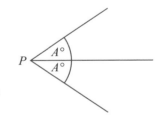

3. If an angle is divided into two, then that angle is equal to the sum of the two angles that make it up.

$$|\angle QPR| = |\angle QPS| + |\angle SPR|$$
$$|\angle QPR| = A° + B°$$

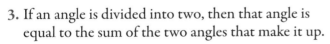

Axiom 4: **Congruent triangles**

We can say that two triangles are congruent if:

1. SAS: Two sides and the angle in between are the same in both.

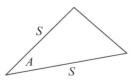

2. ASA: Two angles and a side are the same in both.

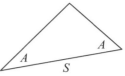

3. SSS: All three sides are the same in both.

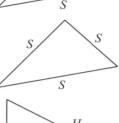

4. RHS: Right angle, hypotenuse and another side.

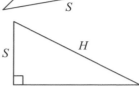

Axiom 5: Given any line *l* and a point *P*, there is exactly one line through *P* that is parallel to *l*.

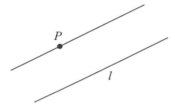

Theorems

- The application of all theorems can be examined.
- Only proofs for theorems 11, 12 and 13 are examinable (marked with *).
- You will be presented with a worded statement of a theorem, without reference to the theorem number.
- Proofs are expected to begin with a diagram, followed by the following headings: 'Given', 'To prove', 'Construction' and 'Proof'.
- You must explain all construction steps fully.
- You may be asked for an example of a proof by contradiction.

Theorem 1: **Vertically opposite angles**

Vertically opposite angles are equal in measure.

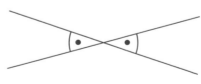

Theorem 2: **Isosceles triangles**

1. In an isosceles triangle, the angles opposite the equal sides are equal.
2. Conversely, if two angles are equal, then the triangle is isosceles.

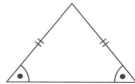

Theorem 3: **Alternate angles**

If a transversal makes equal alternate angles on two lines, then the lines are parallel (and converse).

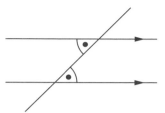

Theorem 4: **Angles in a triangle**

The angles in any triangle add up to 180°.

$$A° + B° + C° = 180°$$

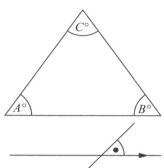

Theorem 5: **Corresponding angles**

Two lines are parallel if, and only if, for any transversal, the corresponding angles are equal.

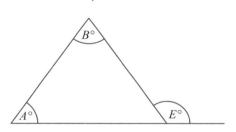

Theorem 6: **Exterior angle**

Each exterior angle of a triangle is equal to the sum of the interior opposite angles.

$$E° = A° + B°$$

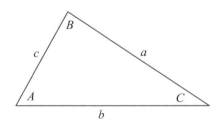

Theorem 7: **Angle–side relationship**

1. In a triangle, the angle opposite the greater of two sides is greater than the angle opposite the lesser side.

2. Conversely, the side opposite the greater of two angles is greater than the side opposite the lesser angle.

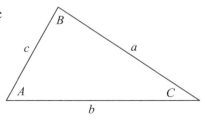

Theorem 8: **Triangle inequality**

Any two sides of a triangle are together greater than the third.

$$a + b > c$$
$$b + c > a$$
$$a + c > b$$

Theorem 9: **Parallelograms**

In a parallelogram, opposite sides are equal and opposite angles are equal. Two converses of this theorem are true:

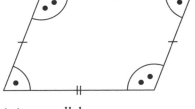

1. If the opposite angles of a quadrilateral are equal, then it is a parallelogram.
2. If the opposite sides of a quadrilateral are equal, then it is a parallelogram.

Corollary: A diagonal divides a parallelogram into two congruent triangles.

Theorem 10: **Diagonals of a parallelogram**

The diagonals of a parallelogram bisect each other.

Converse:

If the diagonals of a quadrilateral bisect one another, then it is a parallelogram.

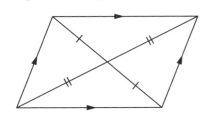

*Theorem 11: **Transversals**

If three parallel lines cut off equal segments on some transversal line, then they will cut off equal segments on any other transversal.

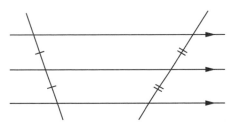

*Theorem 12: **Proportional sides**

Let *ABC* be a triangle. If a line *XY* is parallel to *BC* and cuts [*AB*] in the ratio *s* : *t*, then it also cuts [*AC*] in the same ratio.

Converse:

If a line *XY* cuts the sides *AB* and *AC* in the same ratio, then it is parallel to *BC*.

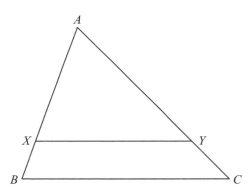

*Theorem 13: **Similar triangles**

If two triangles are similar, then their sides are proportional, in order.

$$\frac{|PQ|}{|AB|} = \frac{|PR|}{|AC|} = \frac{|QR|}{|BC|}$$

Converse:

If the corresponding sides of two triangles are proportional, then they are similar.

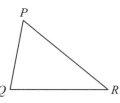
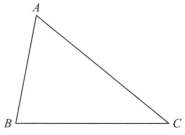

Theorem 14: **Theorem of Pythagoras**

In a right-angled triangle, the square of the
hypotenuse is the sum of the squares of
the other two sides.

$$|AC|^2 = |AB|^2 + |BC|^2$$

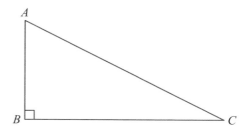

Theorem 15: **Converse to Pythagoras**

If the square of one side is the sum of the squares of the other two, then the angle
opposite the first side is a right angle.

Theorem 16: **Area**

For a triangle, base $\times$ height does not depend on the
choice of base.

Definition:
The area of a triangle is half the base by the height,
regardless of which side you choose as the base.

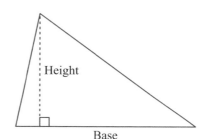

Theorem 17: **Parallelogram bisector**

A diagonal of a parallelogram bisects the area.

$$\text{Area} \triangle ABD = \text{Area} \triangle CDB$$

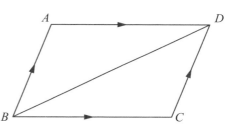

Theorem 18: **Area of a parallelogram**

The area of a parallelogram is the base $\times$ height.

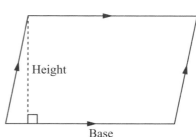

Theorem 19: **Circle theorem**

The angle at the centre of a circle standing on a given
arc is twice the angle at any point of the circle standing
on the same arc.

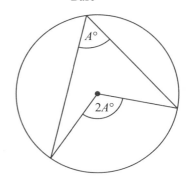

Corollary 1: All angles at points of a circle standing on the same arc are equal.

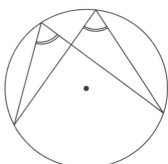

Corollary 2: Each angle in a semicircle is a right angle.

Corollary 3: If the angle standing on a chord $[BC]$ at some point on the circle is a right angle, then $[BC]$ is a diameter.

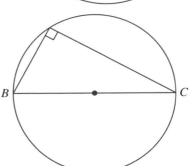

Corollary 4: If *ABCD* is a cyclic quadrilateral, then opposite angles sum to 180°.

$$A° + C° = 180°$$
$$B° + D° = 180°$$

Converse:
If the opposite angles of a quadrilateral sum to 180°, the quadrilateral is cyclic.

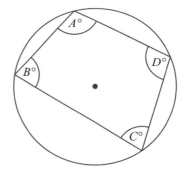

Theorem 20: **Tangents**

1. Each tangent is perpendicular to the radius that goes to the point of contact.
2. If *P* lies on the circle *s*, and a line *l* is perpendicular to the radius at *P*, then *l* is a tangent to *s*.

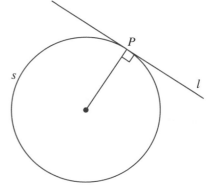

Corollary: If two circles intersect at one point only, then the two centres and the point of contact are collinear.

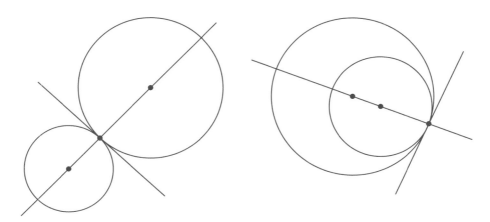

Theorem 21: **Perpendicular bisector of a chord**

1. The perpendicular from the centre of a circle to a chord bisects the chord.
2. The perpendicular bisector of a chord passes through the centre of the circle.

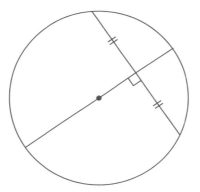

When solving questions which involve diagrams, it is often helpful to do rough copies, in pencil, of the diagram on a separate piece of paper. This allows you to mark things on the diagram and try different approaches, **without drawing on the original image**. This can be useful if you take the wrong approach the first time. You still have a clean diagram to work from.

Proof of theorems

Theorem 11: If three parallel lines cut off equal segments on some transversal line, then they will cut off equal segments on any other transversal.

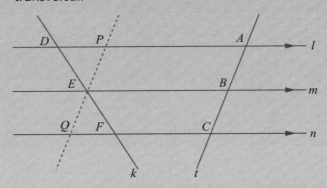

Given: Three parallel lines, l, m and n, intersecting the transversal, t, at the points A, B and C such that $|AB| = |BC|$. Another transversal, k, intersects the lines at D, E and F.

To prove: $|DE| = |EF|$

Construction: Through E, construct a line parallel to t and intersecting l at the point P and n at the point Q.

Proof: $PEBA$ and $EQCB$ are parallelograms.

Then $|PE| = |AB|$ and $|EQ| = |BC|$ (opposite sides)

But $|AB| = |BC|$

So $|PE| = |EQ|$

In $\triangle DEP$ and $\triangle FEQ$

$|PE| = |EQ|$

$|\angle PED| = |\angle FEQ|$ (vertically opposite angles)

$|\angle DPE| = |\angle FQE|$ (alternate angles)

$\therefore \triangle DEP$ and $\triangle FEQ$ are congruent   (ASA rule)

$\therefore |DE| = |EF|$

Theorem 12:   Let *ABC* be a triangle. If a line *XY* is parallel to *BC* and cuts [*AB*] in the ratio *s* : *t*, then it also cuts [*AC*] in the same ratio.

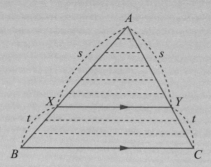

Given: The triangle *ABC* with *XY* parallel to *BC*.

To prove: $\dfrac{|AX|}{|XB|} = \dfrac{|AY|}{|YC|}$

Construction: Divide [*AX*] into *s* equal parts and [*XB*] into *t* equal parts.

Draw a line parallel to *BC* through each point of the division.

Proof: The parallel lines make intercepts of equal length along the line [*AC*]. (converse of transerval theorem)

∴ [*AY*] is divided into *s* equal intercepts and [*YC*] is divided into *t* equal intercepts.

∴ $\dfrac{|AY|}{|YC|} = \dfrac{s}{t}$

But $\dfrac{|AX|}{|XB|} = \dfrac{s}{t}$

∴ $\dfrac{|AX|}{|XB|} = \dfrac{|AY|}{|YC|}$

Theorem 13: If two triangles, *ABC* and *DEF,* are similar, then their sides are proportional in order:

$$\frac{|AB|}{|DE|} = \frac{|BC|}{|EF|} = \frac{|AC|}{|DF|}$$

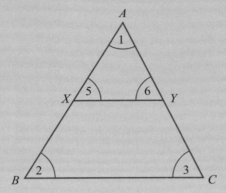
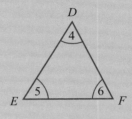

Given: The triangles *ABC* and *DEF* in which $|\angle 1| = |\angle 4|$, $|\angle 2| = |\angle 5|$ and $|\angle 3| = |\angle 6|$.

To prove: $\dfrac{|AB|}{|DE|} = \dfrac{|BC|}{|EF|} = \dfrac{|AC|}{|DF|}$

Construction: Mark the point *X* on [*AB*] such that $|AX| = |DE|$.

Mark the point *Y* on [*AC*] such that $|AY| = |DF|$.

Join *XY*.

Proof: The triangles *AXY* and *DEF* are congruent.   (SAS)

∴ $|\angle AXY| = |\angle DEF| = |\angle 5|$ (corresponding angles)

∴ $|\angle AXY| = |\angle ABC|$

∴ $XY \parallel BC$ (corresponding angles)

∴ $\dfrac{|AB|}{|AX|} = \dfrac{|AC|}{|AY|}$ (a line parallel to one side divides the other side in the same ratio)

∴ $\dfrac{|AB|}{|DE|} = \dfrac{|AC|}{|DF|}$

Similarly, it can be proven that ∴ $\dfrac{|AB|}{|DE|} = \dfrac{|BC|}{|EF|}$

∴ $\dfrac{|AB|}{|DE|} = \dfrac{|BC|}{|EF|} = \dfrac{|AC|}{|DF|}$

You must learn, and be able to reproduce, the proofs for theorems 11, 12 and 13.

Proof by contradiction

This method of proof takes a proposition of the form

If certain conditions, **then** a result will follow.

And examines the consequences of assuming that

If certain conditions, **then** the *opposite* result will follow.

To prove:	A triangle has at most one obtuse angle.
Proof:	Consider a triangle with angles A, B and C.

Assume that the opposite of the 'to prove' statement is true, i.e. the triangle has **more** than one obtuse angle.

Suppose A and B are both obtuse.

∴ A is more than 90° and B is more than 90°.

∴ A + B is more than 90° + 90°, which is more than 180°.

But this is impossible, as the *three* angles must add up to 180°.

Therefore, it is not possible for the triangle to have two obtuse angles.

Therefore, a triangle has at most one obtuse angle.

The method of 'proof by contradiction' is a vital skill that can be easily transferred to other aspects of this course. It does not relate purely to the topic of geometry.

Application and use of theorems

You must know all of the theorems very well and be able to apply them when solving geometric problems.

- Be aware that there may be more than one method of proof for answering questions by the application of theorems.
- Many geometry problems will involve aspects of trigonometry.

Example

O is a point inside an acute-angled triangle ABC. The feet of the perpendiculars from O to BC, CA and AB respectively are P, Q and R. Prove that:

$$|PB|^2 - |PC|^2 = |OB|^2 - |OC|^2$$

Solution

Start by drawing a diagram of the triangle.

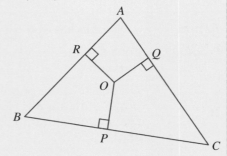

Construction

Join O to B.
Join O to C.
Join O to A.

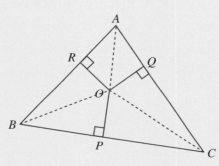

Proof

In $\triangle BOP$, $|PB|^2 = |OB|^2 - |OP|^2$
    (Pythagoras' theorem).

In $\triangle POC$, $|PC|^2 = |OC|^2 - |OP|^2$
    (Pythagoras' theorem).

Subtracting $|PC|^2$ from $|PB|^2$ gives:

$$|PB|^2 - |PC|^2 = [|OB|^2 - |OP|^2] - [|OC|^2 - |OP|^2]$$
$$|PB|^2 - |PC|^2 = |OB|^2 - |OP|^2 - |OC|^2 + |OP|^2$$
$$\therefore |PB|^2 - |PC|^2 = |OB|^2 - |OC|^2$$

It is important to give reasons and explanations for statements made during a proof. This shows that you understand the steps you are taking and thus will help ensure that you get maximum marks in a question.

In the diagram, l_1, l_2, l_3 and l_4 are parallel lines that make intercepts of equal length on the transversal, k.

FG is parallel to k and HG is parallel to ED.

Prove that the triangles $\triangle CDE$ and $\triangle FGH$ are congruent.

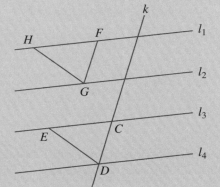

Solution

Construction:

Label the points A and B on the diagram.

$|AB| = |CD|$	(given)
$|AB| = |FG|$	(opposite sides of a parallelogram)
$\therefore\ |CD| = |FG|$	(marked with double dashes)

$HG \parallel ED$	(given)
$CD \parallel AB \parallel FG$	(given)
$\therefore\ |\angle EDC| = |\angle HGF|$	(corresponding angles)
	(marked with a •)

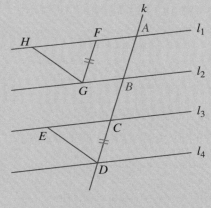

Similarly,

$HF \parallel EC$	(given)
$CD \parallel FG$	(given)
$\therefore\ |\angle ECD| = |\angle HFG|$	(corresponding angles)
	(marked with an *)
$\therefore\ \triangle CDE \equiv \triangle FGH$	(ASA)

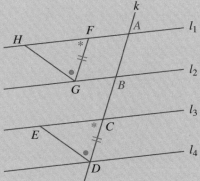

In the triangle ABC, $|AB| = q$ and $|CB| = p$.

Find the shortest distance from the vertex, B, to the side $[AC]$, in terms of p and q.

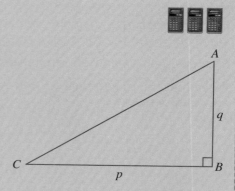

Solution

Draw a perpendicular line from B to $[AC]$. Label this new point D.

Mark this new length x.

This is the required shortest distance.

Using Pythagoras' theorem on $\triangle ABC$, we find:

$$|AC| = \sqrt{p^2 + q^2}$$

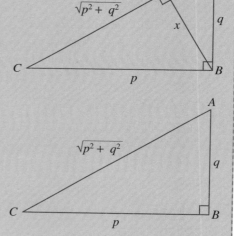

Consider $\triangle ABC$ and $\triangle ADB$:

$|\angle CAB| = |\angle BAD|$ (common angle)

$|\angle CBA| = |\angle BDA|$ (both 90°)

$\therefore$ $\triangle ABC$ and $\triangle ADB$ are similar.

$\therefore$ Their sides are in proportion.

$$\frac{|BD|}{|CB|} = \frac{|AB|}{|AC|}$$

$$\frac{x}{p} = \frac{q}{\sqrt{p^2 + q^2}}$$

$$x = \frac{pq}{\sqrt{p^2 + q^2}}$$

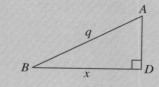

Alternative method:

Area of $\triangle ABC = \dfrac{1}{2}$ (base) ($\perp$ height)

Area of $\triangle ABC = \dfrac{1}{2}\left(\sqrt{p^2 + q^2}\right)(x)$

Area of $\triangle ABC = \dfrac{1}{2}(p)(q)$

$\therefore \quad \dfrac{1}{2}\left(\sqrt{p^2 + q^2}\right)(x) = \dfrac{1}{2}(p)(q)$

$\left(\sqrt{p^2 + q^2}\right)(x) = (p)(q)$

$x = \dfrac{pq}{\sqrt{p^2 + q^2}}$

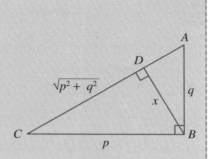

In the diagram, P_1Q_1, P_2Q_2 and P_3Q_3 are parallel and so are Q_1P_2 and Q_2P_3.

Prove that $|P_1Q_1| \times |P_3Q_3| = |P_2Q_2|^2$.

Solution

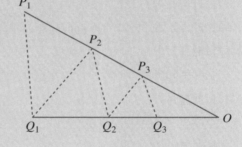

$\dfrac{|OP_3|}{|OP_2|} = \dfrac{|OQ_2|}{|OQ_1|}$ Since $P_3Q_2 \parallel P_2Q_1$.

$\dfrac{|OP_2|}{|OP_1|} = \dfrac{|OQ_2|}{|OQ_1|}$ Since $P_2Q_2 \parallel P_1Q_1$.

$\therefore \quad \dfrac{|OP_3|}{|OP_2|} = \dfrac{|OP_2|}{|OP_1|}$ ①

Since $P_1Q_1 \parallel P_2Q_2 \parallel P_3Q_3$, $\triangle P_1Q_1O$, $\triangle P_2Q_2O$ and $\triangle P_3Q_3O$ are similar and therefore their sides are in proportion.

$\dfrac{|OP_2|}{|OP_1|} = \dfrac{|P_2Q_2|}{|P_1Q_1|}$ ②   Since $\triangle P_1Q_1O$ and $\triangle P_2Q_2O$ are similar triangles.

$\therefore \quad \dfrac{|OP_3|}{|OP_2|} = \dfrac{|P_2Q_2|}{|P_1Q_1|}$ ③   (comparing ① and ②)

$\dfrac{|OP_3|}{|OP_2|} = \dfrac{|P_3Q_3|}{|P_2Q_2|}$ ④   Since $\triangle P_2Q_2O$ and $\triangle P_3Q_3O$ are similar triangles.

$\therefore \quad \dfrac{|P_2Q_2|}{|P_1Q_1|} = \dfrac{|P_3Q_3|}{|P_2Q_2|}$ (comparing ③ and ④)

$\therefore \quad |P_1Q_1| \times |P_3Q_3| = |P_2Q_2|^2$

In the diagram, [PQ] is a bisector of |∠TPR|.

Prove that |QP| = |QR|.

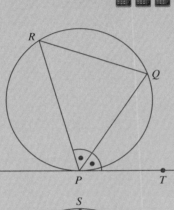

Solution

You need to prove that △PQR is isosceles.

Construct the line [PS] perpendicular to the tangent.

Since this line is perpendicular to the tangent, it must be a diameter of the circle.

∴ |∠PQS| = 90° (angle in a semicircle is 90°)

Label angles 1, 2, 3, 4, 5 as in the diagram.

|∠1| + |∠2| = 90° (remaining angles in a right-angled triangle)

|∠1| + |∠4| = 90° (since PT is a tangent)

∴ |∠2| = |∠4|

|∠2| = |∠3| (both standing on arc PQ)

∴ |∠3| = |∠4|

|∠4| = |∠5| (given)

∴ |∠3| = |∠5|

∴ △PQR is isosceles.

∴ |QP| = |QR|

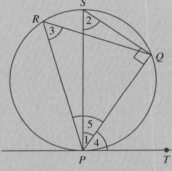

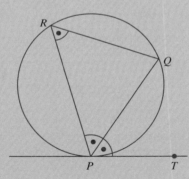

Labelling the angles with numbers often makes the solution simpler.

ABC is a triangle.
D is a point on BC such that AD ⊥ BC.

E is a point on AC such that BE ⊥ AC.

AD and BE intersect at O.

Prove that |∠DOC| = |∠DEC|.

Solution

Construction:

Draw a circle such that [OC] is the diameter.

Proof:

Since |∠ODC| and |∠OEC| are both 90°, the points D and E are both on the circumference of the circle.

∴ O, D, C and E are concyclic.

This means they are four points on the same circle.

Construct the chord [DE].

∠DOC and ∠DEC are both standing on the arc DC.

∴ |∠DOC| = |∠DEC|

From the corollary that all angles at the circle standing on the same arc are all equal.

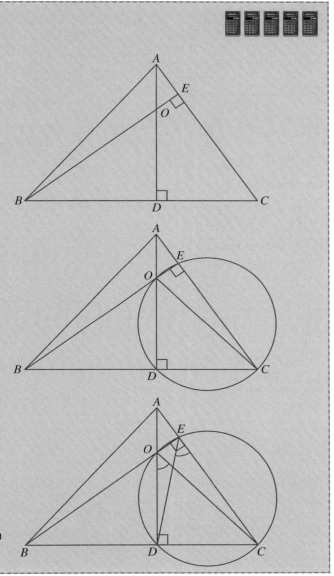

A set of points are said to be **concyclic** if they lie on a common circle.

In the diagram to the right, the points A, B and C are concyclic.

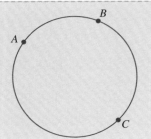

The incircle of the triangle *ABC* has centre *O* and touches the sides at *P*, *Q* and *R*, as shown.

Prove that:

$$|\angle PQR| = \frac{1}{2}(|\angle CAB| + |\angle CBA|)$$

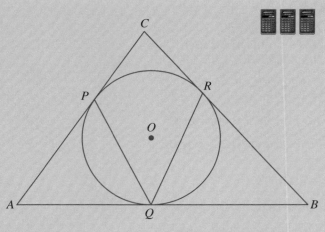

Solution

Construction:

Draw a radius from the centre to the points *P* and *R*.

Label angles 1, 2, 3, 4, 5 as in the diagram.

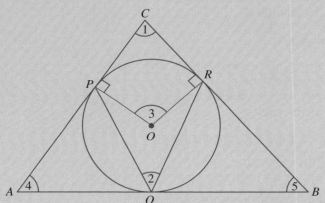

Proof:

These radii meet the sides perpendicularly, since the circle touches the sides of the triangle.

$|\angle 1| + |\angle 4| + |\angle 5| = 180°$ (three angles of a triangle)

$|\angle 1| + |\angle 3| = 180°$ (remaining angles in quadrilateral *CPOR*)

$\therefore |\angle 3| = |\angle 4| + |\angle 5|$

$\quad 2|\angle 2| = |\angle 3|$ (standing on the same arc *PR*)

$\therefore \quad 2|\angle 2| = |\angle 4| + |\angle 5|$ (÷ 2)

$\quad |\angle 2| = \frac{1}{2}(|\angle 4| + |\angle 5|)$ (divide both sides by 2)

$\therefore |\angle PQR| = \frac{1}{2}(|\angle CAB| + |\angle CBA|)$

Alternative method:

$$|\angle OQA| = |\angle OPA| = 90° \quad \text{(radius} \perp \text{tangent)}$$

$\therefore$ O, Q, A, P are concyclic,

so they are four points on the same circle.

Thus, we can construct this circle on the diagram.

$$|\angle OQP| = |\angle OAP| \qquad \text{(standing on same arc } OP)$$

$$= \frac{1}{2}|\angle PAQ| \qquad \text{(since [AO] is the bisector of } \angle PAQ)$$

Similarly, $|\angle OQR| = \frac{1}{2}|\angle QBR|$.

$$\therefore |\angle OQP| + |\angle OQR| = \frac{1}{2}|\angle PAQ| + \frac{1}{2}|\angle QBR|$$

$$\therefore |\angle PQR| = \frac{1}{2}(|\angle CAB| + |\angle CBA|)$$

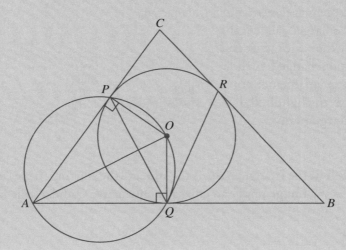

☐ To know how to find the centre of enlargement
☐ To know how to find the scale factor of enlargement
☐ To be able to solve problems involving missing sides and the area of enlarged shapes
☐ To be able to complete all 22 constructions
☐ To be able to use your knowledge of constructions to solve practical problems

Enlargements

An **enlargement** changes the size of a shape to give a similar image. To enlarge a shape, we need a centre of enlargement and a scale factor.

When a shape is enlarged, all lengths are multiplied by the scale factor and all angles remain unchanged. A slide projector makes an enlargement of a shape. In this case, the light bulb is the **centre of enlargement**.

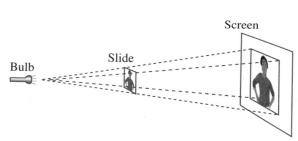

Ray method

In the diagram below, the triangle ABC is the **object** (the starting shape) and the triangle $A'B'C'$ is the **image** under an enlargement, centre O and a scale factor of $\frac{1}{2}$.

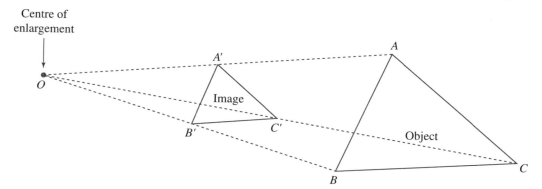

The rays have been drawn from the centre of enlargement, O, to each vertex and beyond. The distance from the centre of enlargement, O, to each vertex on triangle ABC was measured and multiplied by $\frac{1}{2}$. Thus, $|OA'| = \frac{1}{2}|OA|$, $|OB'| = \frac{1}{2}|OB|$ and $|OC'| = \frac{1}{2}|OC|$.

Also, $|A'B'| = \frac{1}{2}|AB|, |A'C'| = \frac{1}{2}|AC|$ and $|B'C'| = \frac{1}{2}|BC|$.

Note: All measurements are made from the centre of enlargement, O.

Properties of enlargements:

1. The shape of the image is the same as the shape of the object (only the size has changed).
2. The amount by which a figure is enlarged is called the **scale factor** and is denoted by k.
3. Image length = k(object length)   or $k = \dfrac{\text{Image length}}{\text{Object length}}$
4. Area of image = k^2(area of object)   or $k^2 = \dfrac{\text{Area of image}}{\text{Area of object}}$

1. The scale factor can be less than 1 (i.e. $0 < k < 1$). In these cases, the image will be smaller than the object. Though smaller, the image is still called an enlargement.
2. The centre of enlargement can be a vertex on the object figure, inside it or outside.

To find the centre of enlargement, do the following:

1. Choose two points on the image and their corresponding points on the original figure.
2. From each of these points on the larger figure, draw a line to the corresponding point on the smaller figure.
3. Produce these lines until they intersect at a point. This point is the centre of enlargement.

Example

Triangle OAB is the image of triangle OXY under the enlargement, centre O, with $|XY| = 8, |OX| = 10$ and $|AB| = 18$.

(i) Find the scale factor of the enlargement.
(ii) Find $|XA|$.
(iii) The area of triangle OAB is 101·25 square units. Find the area of triangle OXY.

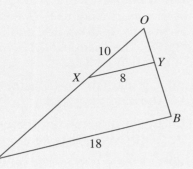

Solution

(i) Since we are told that the triangle OAB is the image of the triangle OXY:

$$\text{Scale factor} = k = \frac{\text{Image length}}{\text{Object length}} = \frac{|AB|}{|XY|} = \frac{18}{8} = \frac{9}{4}$$

(ii) $\text{Scale factor} = k = \dfrac{\text{Image length}}{\text{Object length}}$

$$k = \frac{9}{4} = \frac{\text{Image length}}{\text{Object length}} = \frac{|OA|}{|OX|}$$

$$\frac{9}{4} = \frac{|OA|}{10}$$

$$9(10) = 4|OA|$$

$$22.5 = |OA|$$

$$|OA| = |XA| + |OX|$$

$$22 \cdot 5 = |XA| + 10$$

$$\therefore\ 12 \cdot 5 = |XA|$$

(iii)

$$k^2 = \frac{\text{Area of image}}{\text{Area of object}}$$

$$\left(\frac{9}{4}\right)^2 = \frac{\text{Area of } \triangle OAB}{\text{Area of } \triangle OXY}$$

$$\frac{81}{16} = \frac{101 \cdot 25}{\text{Area of } \triangle OXY}$$

$$81(\text{area of } \triangle OXY) = 16(101 \cdot 25)$$

$$\text{Area of } \triangle OXY = \frac{1{,}620}{81}$$

$$\text{Area of } \triangle OXY = 20 \text{ sq. units}$$

Two triangles are drawn on a square grid, as shown. The points P, Q, R, X and Z are on vertices of the triangles, and the point Y lies on [PR]. The triangle PQR is an enlargement of the triangle XYZ.

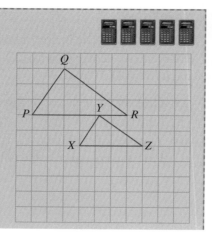

(i) Calculate the scale factor of the enlargement, showing your work.

(ii) By construction or otherwise, locate the centre of enlargement on the diagram.

(iii) Calculate |YR| in grid units.

Solution

(i) Since we are told that the triangle *PQR* is an enlargement of the triangle *XYZ*, we take triangle *XYZ* as the object and triangle *PQR* as the image.

$$\text{Scale factor} = k = \frac{\text{Image length}}{\text{Object length}} = \frac{|PR|}{|XZ|} = \frac{6}{4} = \frac{3}{2}$$

(ii) To find the centre of enlargement:

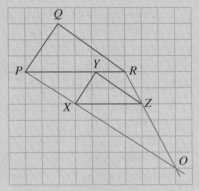

1. Choose two points on the image and their corresponding points on the original image.

2. From each of these points on the larger figure, draw a line to the corresponding point on the smaller figure.

3. Produce these lines until they intersect at the point *O*, which is the centre of enlargement.

(iii) Drop a vertical down from *Q* and *Y* and mark the new points *A* and *B*, respectively.

Since triangle *PQR* is an enlargement of triangle *XYZ*, we know that the triangles are similar and so $\angle PRQ = \angle XZY$.

∴ $\triangle QAR$ and $\triangle YBZ$ are similar.

∴ $\dfrac{|QA|}{|YB|} = \dfrac{|AR|}{|BZ|}$ (by theorem)

$\dfrac{3}{2} = \dfrac{4}{|BZ|}$

$3|BZ| = 4(2)$

$|BZ| = \dfrac{8}{3}$

$|BZ|$ is one unit longer than $|YR|$.

∴ $|YR| = |BZ| - 1$

∴ $|YR| = \dfrac{8}{3} - 1$

∴ $|YR| = \dfrac{5}{3}$

key point

An alternative method would be to use trigonometry.

exam focus

Most students were not successful in answering part **(iii)**. Consequently it was awarded only 5 marks, while part **(i)** was awarded 15 marks.

Constructions

There are 22 constructions that you must be able to perform on the Leaving Certificate Higher Level course.

1. Bisector of an angle, using only a compass and straight edge
2. Perpendicular bisector of a segment, using only a compass and straight edge
3. Line perpendicular to a given line l, passing through a given point not on l
4. Line perpendicular to a given line l, passing through a given point on l
5. Line parallel to a given line, through a given point
6. Division of a line segment into two or three equal segments without measuring it
7. Division of a line segment into any number of equal segments without measuring it
8. Line segment of a given length on a given ray
9. Angle of a given number of degrees with a given ray as one arm
10. Triangle, given length of three sides (SSS)
11. Triangle, given two sides and the included angle (SAS)
12. Triangle, given two angles and the common side (ASA)
13. Right-angled triangle, given length of hypotenuse and one other side (RHS)
14. Right-angled triangle, given one side and one of the acute angles
15. Rectangle, given side lengths
16. Circumcentre and circumcircle of a given triangle, using only a straight edge and compass
17. Incentre and incircle of a given triangle, using only a straight edge and compass
18. Angle of 60° without using a protractor or set square
19. Tangent to a given circle at a given point on it
20. Parallelogram, given the length of the sides and the measure of the angles
21. Centroid of a triangle
22. Orthocentre of a triangle

- The steps required for completing each of these constructions are detailed in your textbook.
- Computer simulations of these constructions can be found at www.mathopenref.com.
- Any work involving accurate constructions requires a good pencil, eraser, a compass, a ruler, a set square and a protractor.

It is important to show **all** construction lines or marks you make at any stage during the construction. Erasing any of these may result in marks being lost in an exam.

Example

Construct $\sqrt{3}$.

Solution

Consider a right-angled triangle, one side of which is 1 unit in length and with a hypotenuse of 2 units.

By applying Pythagoras' theorem, we find the third side equals $\sqrt{3}$.

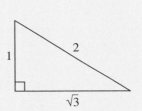

Draw a rough sketch of this triangle.

Now construct this triangle accurately.

Start by drawing a vertical line 1 unit in length and draw a horizontal line out from its base.

Draw an arc 2 units in length from the top of the vertical line to the horizontal line.

This is the hypotenuse.

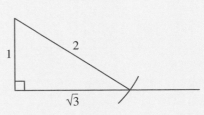

The length marked off the bottom equals $\sqrt{3}$.

You may be asked to construct $\sqrt{3}$ in the exam. **You must also be able to construct $\sqrt{2}$ accurately.** In this case, construct a right-angled isosceles triangle with perpendicular sides 1 unit in length. The hypotenuse of this triangle equals $\sqrt{2}$.

exam
Q

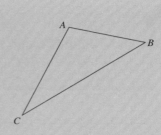

(i) Construct the circumcircle of the triangle *ABC* using only a compass and straight edge. Show all construction lines clearly.

(ii) State the condition(s) under which the circumcentre of a triangle will lie inside the triangle. Justify your answer.

Solution

(i) Construct the perpendicular bisectors of [*AB*] and [*AC*].

Produce these bisectors until they meet at a point, *K*. *K* is the circumcentre.

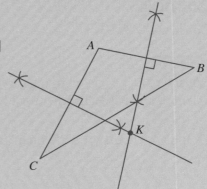

With *K* as the centre and radius $r = |KA|$, draw a circle. This circle will pass through the three vertices of the triangle.

The circle drawn is the circumcircle.

(|*KB*| and |*KC*| will also be radii of the circle.)

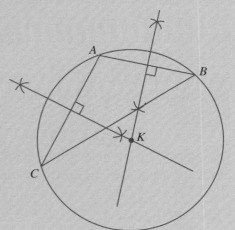

(ii) The triangle in (i) is an obtuse triangle and the circumcentre was outside of the triangle.

If the triangle is right-angled at *A*, the circumcentre is on the line segment [*BC*].

If the triangle is acute (i.e. all three angles are acute angles), the circumcentre will be inside the triangle, as illustrated in the diagram on the right.

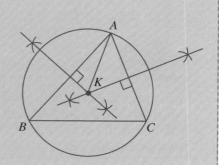

Cavan, Monaghan and Dundalk are three large towns in Ireland. These towns are indicated on the map. Each town has a local hospital for minor needs and emergencies. The Department of Health wants to build an advanced, modern medical facility, which can be shared by the three towns and their surrounding communities.

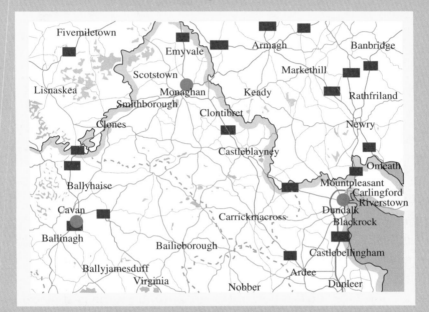

You have been asked to determine the best location for this facility.

(i) What do you think is the most important issue when deciding the location of the new medical facility?

(ii) Accurately construct the most appropriate position of the new medical facility.

(iii) By studying the map, do you think this location is the best place for the new medical facility? Give a reason for your answer.

Solution

(i) The medical facility should be equidistant (the same distance) from each of the three towns.

(ii) The point which is equidistant from each of the towns is known as the circumcentre.

To construct the circumcentre:

1. Join the towns to form a triangle.

2. Label the points C, M and D.

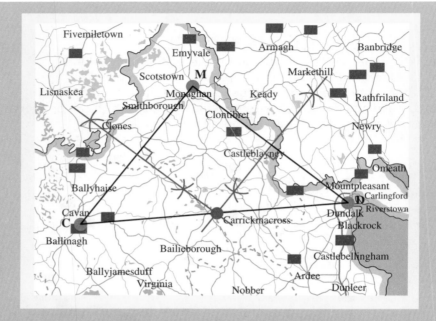

3. Construct the perpendicular bisectors of [*CM*] and [*MD*].

4. The point where these bisectors intersect is the circumcentre of the triangle.

The new medical facility should be placed at the circumcentre, which is indicated by a large blue dot on the map.

(iii) No, I do not think the location of the circumcentre is the best place for the new medical centre, as it is away from the main roads. It may be better to place the medical facility slightly closer to some main roads. Even though it will be physically further away from one town than the others, it may make it quicker to access. Also, one town may have a much bigger population and so it may be wiser to place the medical centre closer to that town.

OR

Yes, I think the location of the circumcentre is the best place for the new medical centre, as it is an equal distance from each of the towns, so it is the fairest place to put it.

In the exam, when you are asked for your opinion you must be aware that more than one answer can be valid. Whatever opinion you give, it is important that you give reasons to back it up.

Fintan has a triangular garden, as shown.
He intends to build a circular pond within
the garden.

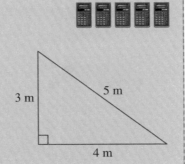

(i) Describe how Fintan would determine where
the largest pond can be placed.

(ii) Find the radius of the largest pond that
could fit.

(iii) Why might Fintan choose not to build the largest
pond possible? Suggest a practical change he
should make.

Solution

(i) To create the largest circular pool, Fintan
would need to create a circle that touches all
sides of the plot of land.

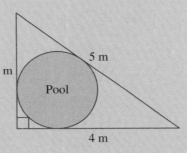

Therefore, Fintan needs to construct the
incircle of the triangle.

(ii) Label the vertices A, B and C.

Draw a radius perpendicularly to each side. Join each vertex to the centre of
the circle, O, to divide the big triangle into three smaller triangles.

Area of $\triangle ABC$ = Area of $\triangle AOB$ + Area of $\triangle BOC$ + Area of $\triangle AOC$

$\frac{1}{2}(4)(3) = \frac{1}{2}(3)(r) + \frac{1}{2}(4)(r) + \frac{1}{2}(5)(r)$ (×)

$12 = 3r + 4r + 5r$

$12 = 12r$

$1 = r$

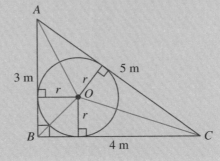

Therefore, the radius length is 1 m.

There are other ways to solve this question, using geometry and
trigonometry.

(iii) If Fintan chooses to build the circular pond, as in the diagram, he would have no space to walk around the pond. He should reduce the radius of the pond to allow space for a path around the pond.

Other suggestions would be acceptable answers as long as they are practical, functional and realistic for this situation.

5 Trigonometry I

☐ To learn how to solve triangles to find missing sides or angles
☐ To learn how to find the area of a triangle
☐ To learn how to find the area and perimeter of a sector of a circle
☐ To learn how to solve trigonometric equations

Formulae for solving triangles

Formulae for right-angled triangles only

(see booklet of formulae and tables page 16)

Pythagoras' theorem:

$$a^2 = b^2 + c^2$$

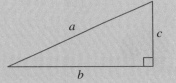

The three trigonometric ratios for a right-angled triangle, $0° < \theta < 90°$, are:

(similar diagram in booklet of formulae and tables page 16)

$$\sin \theta = \frac{O}{H}$$

$$\cos \theta = \frac{A}{H}$$

$$\tan \theta = \frac{O}{A}$$

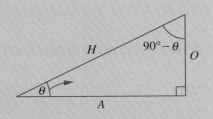

From the diagram, we can see that:

$$\sin(90° - \theta) = \frac{A}{H} = \cos \theta \quad \text{and} \quad \cos(90° - \theta) = \frac{O}{H} = \sin \theta$$

key point

These ratios hold for all values of $\theta \in \mathbb{R}$, not just for $0° < \theta < 90°$.

Formulae for all triangles

(see booklet of formulae and tables page 16)

Sine rule

$$\frac{a}{\sin A} = \frac{b}{\sin B} = \frac{c}{\sin C}$$

or

$$\frac{\sin A}{a} = \frac{\sin B}{b} = \frac{\sin C}{c}$$

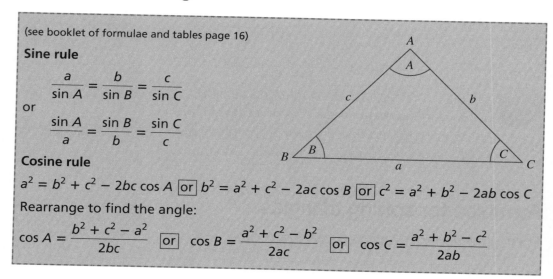

Cosine rule

$$a^2 = b^2 + c^2 - 2bc \cos A \quad \boxed{\text{or}} \quad b^2 = a^2 + c^2 - 2ac \cos B \quad \boxed{\text{or}} \quad c^2 = a^2 + b^2 - 2ab \cos C$$

Rearrange to find the angle:

$$\cos A = \frac{b^2 + c^2 - a^2}{2bc} \quad \boxed{\text{or}} \quad \cos B = \frac{a^2 + c^2 - b^2}{2ac} \quad \boxed{\text{or}} \quad \cos C = \frac{a^2 + b^2 - c^2}{2ab}$$

key point

- When using the **sine rule**, always place the unknown quantity on the top of the left fraction.
- If you need to use the **cosine rule** to find an angle, rearrange the rule first, then substitute the known values. This means that you can enter the solution directly into a calculator.

Use the following flowchart to work out which formula to use

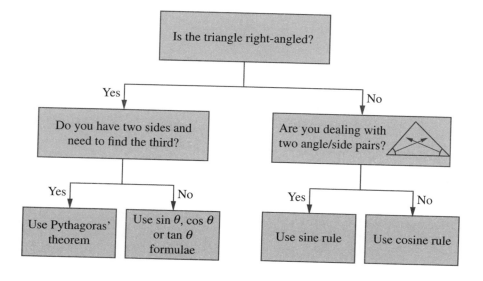

The cosine rule must be used in a non-right-angled triangle if:

- You are given the three sides and need to find an angle.

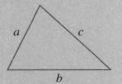

- You are given two sides and the included angle and need to find the third side.

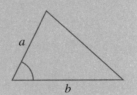

Area of a triangle

(see booklet of formulae and tables page 16)

Given two sides and the angle in between these sides:

$$\text{Area} = \frac{1}{2}ab \sin C = \frac{1}{2}ac \sin B = \frac{1}{2}bc \sin A$$

(see booklet of formulae and tables page 9)

Given the three sides:

$$s = \frac{a + b + c}{2}$$

$$\text{Area} = \sqrt{s(s - a)(s - b)(s - c)}$$

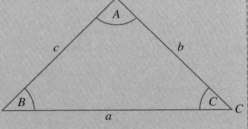

Example

In $\triangle PQR$, $|PR| = \sqrt{8}$ m, $|\angle RPQ| = 30°$ and $|\angle PQR| = 45°$.

(i) Find $|QR|$.

(ii) Show that the area of $\triangle PRQ = 2\cdot7$ m^2, correct to one decimal place.

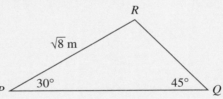

Solution

(i) Use the sine rule to find $|QR|$.

$$\frac{|QR|}{\sin P} = \frac{|PR|}{\sin Q}$$

$$\frac{|QR|}{\sin 30°} = \frac{\sqrt{8}}{\sin 45°}$$

$$|QR| = \frac{\sqrt{8}\sin 30°}{\sin 45°}$$

$$|QR| = \frac{2\sqrt{2}\left(\frac{1}{2}\right)}{\frac{1}{\sqrt{2}}}$$

$$|QR| = 2$$

(ii) Area of $\triangle PQR = \frac{1}{2}|PR| \times |QR| \sin R$.

We need angle R.

The three angles of the triangle sum to 180°.

$R = 180° - 45° - 30°$

$R = 105°$

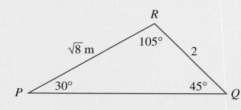

Thus, area $= \frac{1}{2}(\sqrt{8})(2) \sin 105°$

$= 2{\cdot}732050808$

$= 2{\cdot}7 \text{ m}^2$

(correct to one decimal place)

Example

A ball at P is 27 m from the nearer goalpost.

(i) Calculate its distance from the farther goalpost, to the nearest metre.

(ii) Find $|\angle RPQ|$.

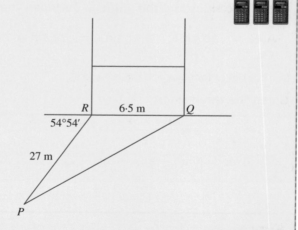

Solution

Draw a triangle by itself to represent the situation.

(i) Find $|PQ|$ (in the diagram, $|PQ| = r$).

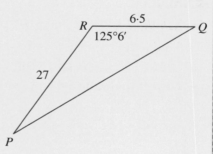

We have two sides and included angle,

∴ use the cosine rule.

$$r^2 = p^2 + q^2 - 2pq \cos R$$

$$= (6.5)^2 + (27)^2 - 2(6.5)(27) \cos 125°6'$$

$$r^2 = 42.25 + 729 - 2(6.5)(27)(-0.5750)$$

$$= 42.25 + 729 + 201.825$$

$$r^2 = 973.075$$

$$r = \sqrt{973.075}$$

$$= 31.1942$$

Thus, $|PQ| = 31$ m.   (correct to the nearest metre)

(ii) Find $|\angle RPQ|$ (from the diagram, $|\angle RPQ| = P$).

We have two sides and non-included angle,

∴ use the sine rule.

$$\frac{\sin P}{p} = \frac{\sin R}{r}$$

$$\frac{\sin P}{6.5} = \frac{\sin 125°6'}{31}$$

$$\sin P = \frac{6.5 \sin 125°6'}{31}$$

$$\sin P = 0.1715475214$$

$$P = \sin^{-1}(0.1715475214)$$

$$P = 9°53' \quad \text{or} \quad P = 9.88°$$

Example

PQRS is a quadrilateral. $|PQ| = 7$, $|QS| = 8$ and $|PS| = 13$.

(i) Show that $|\angle PQS| = 120°$.

(ii) Given that the quadrilateral *PQRS* has an

area of $\dfrac{35\sqrt{3}}{2}$, find the ratio of the area

$\triangle PQS$: area $\triangle QRS$.

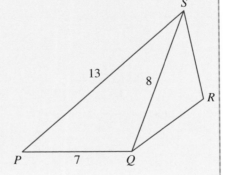

Solution

(i) Redraw $\triangle PQS$.

Using the cosine rule,

$P = 8, Q = 13, S = 7.$

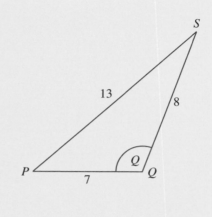

$$\cos Q = \frac{p^2 + s^2 - q^2}{2ps}$$

$$= \frac{8^2 + 7^2 - 13^2}{2(8)(7)}$$

$$= -\frac{1}{2}$$

$$\therefore Q = \cos^{-1}\left(-\frac{1}{2}\right) = 120°$$

Thus, $|\angle PQS| = 120°$.

(ii) Area of $\triangle PQS = \frac{1}{2}ps \sin Q = \frac{1}{2}(8)(7)\sin 120°$

$$= \frac{1}{2}(56)\left(\frac{\sqrt{3}}{2}\right) = \frac{28\sqrt{3}}{2} = 14\sqrt{3}$$

Alternatively, you could find the area using the three sides:

$$s = \frac{a + b + c}{2} = \frac{7 + 8 + 13}{2} = \frac{28}{2} = 14$$

$$\text{Area} = \sqrt{s(s - a)(s - b)(s - c)}$$

$$= \sqrt{14(14 - 7)(14 - 8)(14 - 13)}$$

$$= \sqrt{14(7)(6)(1)}$$

$$= \sqrt{588}$$

$$= 14\sqrt{3}$$

Given: area of quadrilateral $PQRS = \dfrac{35\sqrt{3}}{2}$.

Area of $\triangle QRS$ = Area of quadrilateral $PQRS$ − Area of $\triangle PQS$

$$= \frac{35\sqrt{3}}{2} - 14\sqrt{3}$$

$$= \frac{7\sqrt{3}}{2}$$

Thus:

Area of $\triangle PQS$: Area of $\triangle QRS$

$$= 14\sqrt{3} : \frac{7\sqrt{3}}{2}$$

$$= \qquad 4 : 1$$

In $\triangle ABC$, $|AB| = 3$, $|AC| = 5$ and $|BC| = 7$.

Calculate:

 (i) The measure of the greatest angle of the triangle

 (ii) The area of $\triangle ABC$

(iii) The distance from vertex A to the side $|BC|$

Solution

 (i) The largest angle is opposite the largest side.

   Using the cosine rule:

$$a^2 = b^2 + c^2 - 2bc \cos A$$
$$7^2 = 5^2 + 3^2 - 2(5)(3) \cos A$$
$$49 = 25 + 9 - 30 \cos A$$
$$30 \cos A = 25 + 9 - 49$$
$$30 \cos A = -15$$
$$\cos A = -\frac{1}{2}$$
$$A = \cos^{-1}\left(-\frac{1}{2}\right) = 120°$$

 (ii) Area of $\triangle ABC = \frac{1}{2} bc \sin A = \frac{1}{2}(5)(3) \sin 120° = \frac{1}{2}(5)(3)\left(\frac{\sqrt{3}}{2}\right) = \frac{15\sqrt{3}}{4}$

(iii) Let d be the distance from A to $|BC|$.

   Area of $\triangle ABC = \dfrac{1}{2}$ base $\times$ perpendicular height

$$= \frac{1}{2}(7)(d) = \frac{7}{2}d$$

   From **(ii)**, area of $\triangle ABC = \dfrac{15\sqrt{3}}{4}$

$$\frac{7}{2}d = \frac{15\sqrt{3}}{4}$$
$$14d = 15\sqrt{3} \quad \text{(multiplying both sides by 4)}$$
$$d = \frac{15\sqrt{3}}{14} \quad \text{(divide both sides by 14)}$$

Example

In the diagram, $|PQ| = 4$ cm, $|PR| = 5$ cm, $|QR| = 6$ cm and $|\angle PSR| = 22°$. Find $|PS|$.

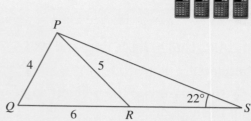

Solution

Two triangles are linked and we need to work on them separately to find $|PS|$.

1. $\triangle PQR$

We need to use the cosine rule to find $|\angle PRQ|$, as we are given three sides.

$$\cos R = \frac{p^2 + q^2 - r^2}{2pq} \quad P = 6, Q = 5, R = 4$$

$$= \frac{6^2 + 5^2 - 4^2}{2(6)(5)}$$

$$= \frac{3}{4}$$

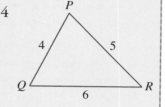

$$R = \cos^{-1}\frac{3}{4} = 41°25'$$

$$\therefore |\angle PRS| = 180° - 41°25' = 138°35'$$

2. $\triangle PRS$

We now use the sine rule to find $|PS|$, as we have two angles and one side.

From the diagram, $|PS| = r$.

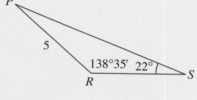

$$\frac{r}{\sin R} = \frac{s}{\sin S} \quad (r \text{ missing; put } r \text{ first})$$

$$\frac{r}{\sin 138°35'} = \frac{5}{\sin 22°}$$

$$r = \frac{5\sin 138°35'}{\sin 22°}$$

$$= 8{\cdot}829663538$$

Thus, $|PS| = 8{\cdot}83$ cm.   (correct to two decimal places)

Circular measure

Angles can be measured in either **degrees** or **radians**. $360° = 2\pi$ radians

Degrees	360°	270°	180°	90°	60°	45°	30°
Radians	2π	$\dfrac{3\pi}{2}$	π	$\dfrac{\pi}{2}$	$\dfrac{\pi}{3}$	$\dfrac{\pi}{4}$	$\dfrac{\pi}{6}$

Throughout the course, you must be able to quickly and easily convert degrees to radians and radians to degrees.

- To **convert degrees to radians**, divide by 180 and multiply by π.
- To **convert radians to degrees**, divide by π and multiply by 180.
  Alternatively, replace π with 180°.

Sectors

(see booklet of formulae and tables, page 9)

If θ is in degrees:

Length of arc: $l = \dfrac{\theta}{360°} \times 2\pi r$

Area of sector: $A = \dfrac{\theta}{360°} \times \pi r^2$

If θ is in radians:

Length of arc: $l = r\theta$

Area of sector: $A = \dfrac{1}{2}r^2\theta$

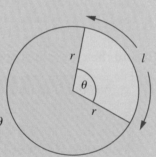

Unit circle

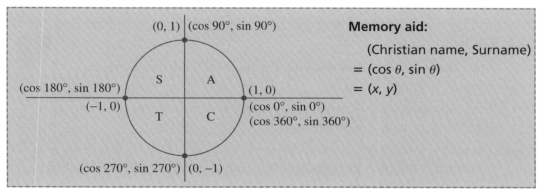

(0, 1) (cos 90°, sin 90°)

(cos 180°, sin 180°)
(−1, 0)

S   A

T   C

(1, 0)
(cos 0°, sin 0°)
(cos 360°, sin 360°)

(cos 270°, sin 270°) (0, −1)

Memory aid:

(Christian name, Surname)
$= (\cos \theta, \sin \theta)$
$= (x, y)$

Angles between 0° and 360°

The trigonometric ratio of an angle between 0° and 360° can be found with the following steps.

1. Make a rough diagram of the angle on a unit circle.

2. Use 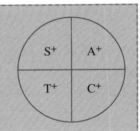 to find whether this ratio is positive or negative.

3. Find its **reference** angle, the acute angle to the *x*-axis.

4. Use a calculator or the tables on page 13 of the booklet of formulae and tables to find the reference angle and use the sign in step 2.

Given the values of sin, cos and tan

Between 0° and 360° there may be two angles with the same trigonometric ratio, e.g. $\cos 120° = -\frac{1}{2}$ and $\cos 240° = -\frac{1}{2}$.

To find the two values, we do the following:

1. Ignore the sign and evaluate the reference angle using the tables or a calculator.

2. From the sign of the given ratio, decide in which quadrants the angles can lie.

3. Using a diagram, state the angles between 0° and 360°.

Example

(i) The radius of a circle is 10 cm. Find the angle subtended at the centre by an arc of length 4π cm.

(ii) Find the area of a sector of a circle of radius 4 cm if the arc of the sector subtended an angle of $\frac{\pi}{3}$ at the centre.

(iii) The area of a sector of a circle of radius r is 12π cm². If the angle subtended at the centre of the circle by this sector is $\frac{2\pi}{3}$, calculate r, the radius of the circle.

Solution

(i) $r = 10, l = 4\pi$. Find θ.

$$l = r\theta$$
$$4\pi = 10\theta$$
$$\theta = \frac{2\pi}{5}$$

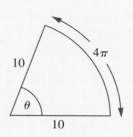

(ii) $r = 4, \theta = \frac{\pi}{3}$. Find A.

$$A = \frac{1}{2}r^2\theta$$
$$= \frac{1}{2}(4)^2\left(\frac{\pi}{3}\right)$$
$$A = \frac{8\pi}{3} \text{ cm}^2$$

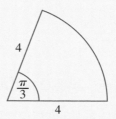

(iii) $A = 12\pi, \theta = \frac{2\pi}{3}$. Find r.

$$A = \frac{1}{2}r^2\theta$$
$$12\pi = \frac{1}{2}r^2\left(\frac{2\pi}{3}\right)$$
$$36 = r^2$$
$$r = 6 \text{ cm}$$

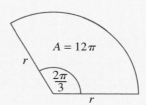

 exam Q

(i) Show that the area, A, of the shaded segment of the circle, of radius r, is given by:

$$A = \frac{1}{2}r^2(\theta - \sin\theta) \qquad (\theta \text{ in radians})$$

(ii) Hence, evaluate the area of the shaded segment when $r = 3\sqrt{2}$ and $\theta = \frac{\pi}{3}$, giving your answer in the form $\left(\frac{\pi}{a} - \frac{\sqrt{a}}{b}\right)$, where a and b are prime numbers.

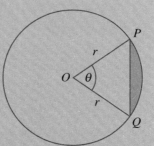

Solution

(i) Area of shaded segment = Area of sector OPQ − Area of $\triangle OPQ$

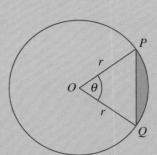

$$= \frac{1}{2}r^2\theta - \frac{1}{2}(r)(r)\sin\theta$$

$$= \frac{1}{2}r^2\theta - \frac{1}{2}r^2\sin\theta$$

$$= \frac{1}{2}r^2(\theta - \sin\theta)$$

(ii) When $r = 3\sqrt{2}$ and $\theta = \dfrac{\pi}{3}$:

Area of shaded segment $= \dfrac{1}{2}(3\sqrt{2})^2\left(\dfrac{\pi}{3} - \sin\dfrac{\pi}{3}\right)$

$$= \frac{1}{2}(18)\left(\frac{\pi}{3} - \frac{\sqrt{3}}{2}\right)$$

$$= 9\left(\frac{\pi}{3} - \frac{\sqrt{3}}{2}\right)$$

In a triangle PQR, $|\angle PQR| = 30°$, $|QR| = 15$ and $|RP| = 5\sqrt{3}$.

Find two values for $|\angle QPR|$ and sketch the two resulting triangles.

Solution

Draw a rough sketch of the triangle PQR.

Use the sine rule:

$$\frac{\sin\theta}{15} = \frac{\sin 30°}{5\sqrt{3}}$$

$$\sin\theta = \frac{15(\sin 30°)}{5\sqrt{3}}$$

$$\sin\theta = \frac{\sqrt{3}}{2}$$

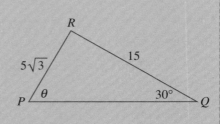

Solve for θ.

Reference angle $= \sin^{-1}\left(\dfrac{\sqrt{3}}{2}\right) = 60°$.

Sin is positive in the first and second quadrants.

So $\theta = 60°$ or $120°$.

Sketches:

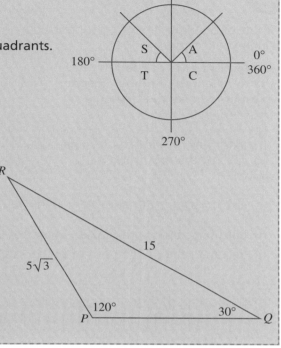

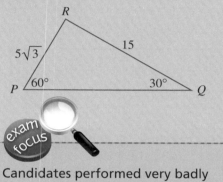

exam focus

Candidates performed very badly on this exam question because they did not know how to get the second value for θ.

exam Q

Given that $\cos 3\theta = -\dfrac{1}{\sqrt{2}}$, solve for all possible values of θ.

Solution

Find the reference angle by ignoring the negative sign.

Reference angle $= \cos^{-1}\left(\dfrac{1}{\sqrt{2}}\right) = 45°$.

Cos is negative in the second and third quadrants.

$$3\theta = 135°, 225°$$

For all possible values of θ:

$3\theta = 135° + n(360°), \ 225° + n(360°), \quad n \in \mathbb{Z}$

$\therefore \ \theta = 45° + n(120°), \quad 75° + n(120°), \quad n \in \mathbb{Z}$ in degrees

or

$\theta = \dfrac{\pi}{4} + n\left(\dfrac{2\pi}{3}\right), \quad \dfrac{5\pi}{12} + n\left(\dfrac{2\pi}{3}\right), \quad n \in \mathbb{Z}$ in radians

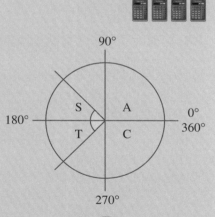

exam focus

This entire question was awarded only 5 marks in the exam.

Roofs of buildings are often supported by frameworks of timber called roof trusses.

A quantity surveyor needs to find the total length of timber needed in order to make the triangular truss shown below.

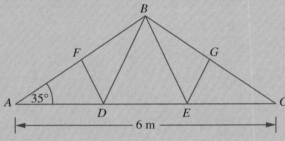

The length of [AC] is 6 metres and the pitch of the roof is 35°, as shown.

$$|AD| = |DE| = |EC| \text{ and } |AF| = |FB| = |BG| = |GC|$$

(i) Calculate the length of [AB], in metres, correct to two decimal places.

(ii) Calculate the total length of timber required to make the truss.

Solution

(i) Draw a line from B vertically down to [AC] this line meets [AC] at the midpoint, H, at right angles.

$$|AH| = 3 \text{ m}$$

$$\cos 35° = \frac{3}{|AB|}$$

$$|AB| = \frac{3}{\cos 35°} = 3.66232$$

$$|AB| = 3.66 \text{ m (to two decimal places)}$$

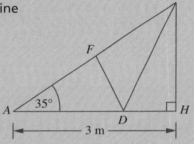

(ii) $|FD|^2 = 1.83^2 + 2^2 - 2(1.83)(2)\cos 35°$

$|FD|^2 = 1.352707$

$|FD| = 1.163 \text{ m}$

$|BD|^2 = 2^2 + 3.66^2 - 2(2)(3.66)\cos 35°$

$|BD|^2 = 5.403214$

$|BD| = 2.326 \text{ m}$

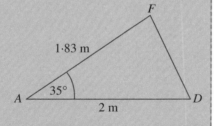

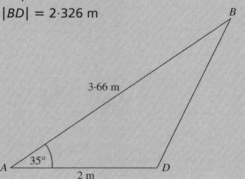

Putting all of the lengths together on the truss:

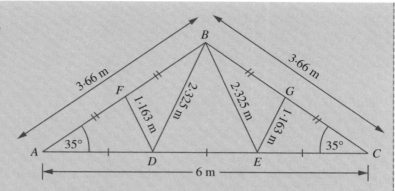

Total length required = 6 + 2(3·66) + 2(1·163) + 2(2·326)

$$= 20·296$$
$$= 20·3 \text{ m}$$

key point

In this question, △ADF and △AEB are similar triangles and so their sides are in proportion. This method could have been used instead of using the cosine rule to find |BE|, which is equal to |BD|.

exam Q

(i) Show that the equation 15 cos² x = 13 + sin x may be written as a quadratic equation in sin x.

(ii) Solve the quadratic equation for sin x, and hence solve for all values of x where 0° ≤ x ≤ 360°. Give your answer(s) correct to the nearest degree.

Solution

(i) $15 \cos^2 x = 13 + \sin x$

From the booklet of formulae and tables, page 13:

$$1 = \sin^2 x + \cos^2 x$$
$$1 - \sin^2 x = \cos^2 x \qquad \text{(substitute this into the original equation)}$$
$$15(1 - \sin^2 x) = 13 + \sin x$$
$$15 - 15 \sin^2 x = 13 + \sin x$$
$$15 \sin^2 x + \sin x - 2 = 0$$

(ii) Solve: $15 \sin^2 x + \sin x - 2 = 0$

$(5 \sin x + 2)(3 \sin x - 1) = 0$

$\sin x = -\dfrac{2}{5}$ $\sin x = \dfrac{1}{3}$

Reference angle: $\sin^{-1}\left(\dfrac{2}{5}\right) = 24°$ Reference angle: $\sin^{-1}\left(\dfrac{1}{3}\right) = 19°$

(correct to the nearest degree)   (correct to the nearest degree)

Sin is negative in the 3rd and 4th quadrants.   Sin is positive in the 1st and 2nd quadrants.

Mark the reference angle into each quadrant.   Mark the reference angle into each quadrant.

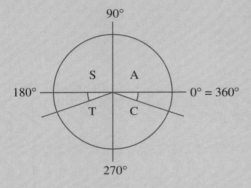   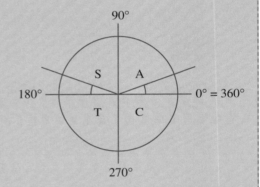

Read angle, x, from 0° to the marked positions: Read angle, x, from 0° to the marked positions:

$x = 180° + 24° = 204°$ $x = 0° + 19° = 19°$

$x = 360° - 24° = 336°$ $x = 180° - 19° = 161°$

$\therefore x = \{19°, 161°, 204°, 336°\}$

You should be very familiar with the trigonometric identities, which are in the book of formulae and tables. Knowing where these formulae are is a big advantage in an exam situation, where they can be used to simplify trigonometric expressions quickly and efficiently.

A chain passes around two circular wheels, as shown. One wheel has a radius of 75 cm and the other has a radius of 15 cm. The centres, *E* and *F*, of the wheels are 120 cm apart.

The chain consists of the common tangent [*AB*], the minor arc *BC*, the common tangent [*CD*] and the major arc *DA*.

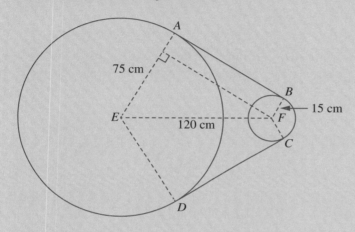

 (i) Find the measure of ∠*AEF*.

 (ii) Find |*AB*| in surd form.

(iii) Find the length of the chain, giving your answer in the form $k\pi + l\sqrt{3}$ where $k, l \in \mathbb{Z}$.

Solution

 (i) Label the point *G*.

$|GE| = |AE| - |AG|$

$|GE| = 75 - 15$

$|GE| = 60$ cm

In △*GEF*:

$$\cos \angle AEF = \frac{|GE|}{|EF|} = \frac{60}{120} = \frac{1}{2}$$

$\therefore \quad \angle AEF = \cos^{-1}\frac{1}{2}$

$\angle AEF = 60°$

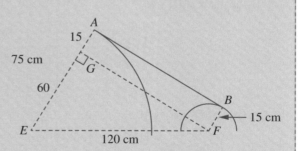

(ii) $|AB| = |GF|$

$\sin \angle AEF = \dfrac{|GF|}{|EF|}$

$\sin 60° = \dfrac{|GF|}{120}$

$120 \sin 60° = |GF|$

$60\sqrt{3} = |GF|$

$\therefore \quad 60\sqrt{3} = |AB|$

(iii) Length of chain = $|$major arc $AD| + |$minor arc $BC| + |AB| + |CD|$

Major arc $\angle AED = 240° = \dfrac{4\pi}{3}$ rad

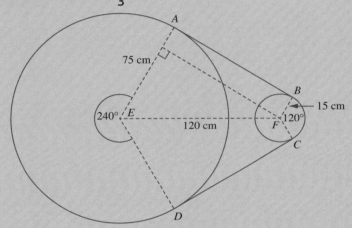

$|$Major arc $AD| = \theta r$	Minor arc $\angle BFC = 120° = \dfrac{2\pi}{3}$ rad
$\qquad = \left(\dfrac{4\pi}{3}\right)(75)$	$|$Minor arc $BC| = \theta r$
$\qquad = 100\pi$ cm	$\qquad = \left(\dfrac{2\pi}{3}\right)(15)$
	$\qquad = 10\pi$ cm

Length of chain $= 100\pi + 10\pi + 60\sqrt{3} + 60\sqrt{3}$

$\qquad\qquad\qquad = (110\pi + 120\sqrt{3})$ cm

Consider the diagram below.

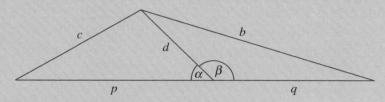

(i) Express $\cos \alpha$ and $\cos \beta$ in terms of the labelled lengths.

(ii) Show that $pb^2 + qc^2 = (p + q)(pq + d^2)$.

Solution

(i)
$$c^2 = d^2 + p^2 - 2dp \cos \alpha$$

$$\therefore \cos \alpha = \frac{d^2 + p^2 - c^2}{2dp}$$

$$b^2 = d^2 + q^2 - 2dq \cos \beta$$

$$\therefore \cos \beta = \frac{d^2 + q^2 - b^2}{2dq}$$

(ii) $\alpha + \beta = 180° \quad \Rightarrow \quad \alpha = 180° - \beta$

$$\cos \alpha = \cos(180° - \beta)$$

$$\cos \alpha = \cos 180° \cos \beta - \sin 180° \sin \beta \quad \text{(tables page 14)}$$

$$\cos \alpha = (-1) \cos \beta - (0) \sin \beta$$

$$\cos \alpha = -\cos \beta$$

$$\therefore \quad \frac{d^2 + p^2 - c^2}{2dp} = -\frac{d^2 + q^2 - b^2}{2dq}$$

$$\frac{d^2 + p^2 - c^2}{2dp} = \frac{-d^2 - q^2 + b^2}{2dq} \quad \text{(multiply both sides by 2dpq)}$$

$$(2dpq)\frac{d^2 + p^2 - c^2}{2dp} = (2dpq)\frac{-d^2 - q^2 + b^2}{2dq}$$

$$(q)(d^2 + p^2 - c^2) = (p)(-d^2 - q^2 + b^2)$$

$$qd^2 + qp^2 - qc^2 = -pd^2 - pq^2 + pb^2 \quad \text{(rearrange terms)}$$

$$pd^2 + qd^2 + qp^2 + pq^2 = pb^2 + qc^2$$

$$d^2(p + q) + pq(p + q) = pb^2 + qc^2$$

$$\therefore \quad (p + q)(pq + d^2) = pb^2 + qc^2$$

exam
Q

The diagram shows a semicircle ABC on $[AC]$ as diameter. The midpoint of $[AC]$ is O, and angle $AOB = \theta$ radians, where $0 < \theta < \dfrac{\pi}{2}$. The area of the segment S_1 cut off by the chord BC is twice the area of the segment S_2 bounded by the chord AB.

Show that $3\theta = \pi + \sin \theta$.

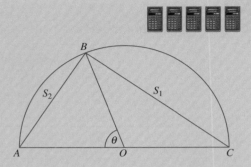

Solution

Area of segment S_2 = Area of sector AOB − Area of triangle AOB

$$S_2 = \frac{1}{2}\theta r^2 - \frac{1}{2}(r)(r)\sin\theta$$

$$S_2 = \frac{1}{2}\theta r^2 - \frac{1}{2}r^2 \sin\theta$$

Area of segment S_1 = Area of sector BOC − Area of triangle BOC

$$S_1 = \frac{1}{2}(\pi - \theta)r^2 - \frac{1}{2}(r)(r)\sin(\pi - \theta)$$

$$= \frac{1}{2}\pi r^2 - \frac{1}{2}\theta r^2 - \frac{1}{2}r^2[\sin\pi\cos\theta - \cos\pi\sin\theta]$$

$$= \frac{1}{2}\pi r^2 - \frac{1}{2}\theta r^2 - \frac{1}{2}r^2[(0)\cos\theta - (-1)\sin\theta]$$

$$= \frac{1}{2}\pi r^2 - \frac{1}{2}\theta r^2 - \frac{1}{2}r^2[\sin\theta]$$

$$= \frac{1}{2}\pi r^2 - \frac{1}{2}\theta r^2 - \frac{1}{2}r^2 \sin\theta$$

Area of segment S_1 = 2 (Area of segment S_2)

$$\therefore\ \frac{1}{2}\pi r^2 - \frac{1}{2}\theta r^2 - \frac{1}{2}r^2 \sin\theta = 2\left[\frac{1}{2}\theta r^2 - \frac{1}{2}r^2 \sin\theta\right]$$

$$\frac{1}{2}\pi r^2 - \frac{1}{2}\theta r^2 - \frac{1}{2}r^2 \sin\theta = \theta r^2 - r^2 \sin\theta \qquad \text{(multiply by 2)}$$

$$\pi r^2 - \theta r^2 - r^2 \sin\theta = 2\theta r^2 - 2r^2 \sin\theta \qquad \text{(divide by } r^2)$$

$$\pi - \theta - \sin\theta = 2\theta - 2\sin\theta \qquad \text{(rearrange terms)}$$

$$\pi + 2\sin\theta - \sin\theta = 2\theta + \theta$$

$$\therefore\ \pi + \sin\theta = 3\theta$$

 exam Q

Two identical discs, of radius 1 unit, are supported by vertical and horizontal plates at P and Q. The diagram shows the discs touching each other and the line of centres is inclined at a radians to the vertical.

Let d be the length of PQ.

(i) Show that $|OQ| = 1 + 2\sin a$.

(ii) Write down a similar expression for $|OP|$ and hence show that
$d^2 = 6 + 4\cos a + 4\sin a$.

(iii) If $a = \dfrac{\pi}{4}$, show that $|OQ| = 1 + \sqrt{2}$ and hence find the area of $\triangle POQ$.

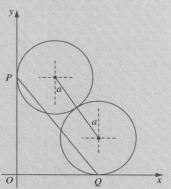

Solution

(i) Let the base of the triangle $= x$.

Then $\qquad |OQ| = 1 + x$

$$\sin a = \frac{x}{2}$$

$$2\sin a = x$$

$\therefore \qquad |OQ| = 1 + 2\sin a$

(ii) Let a side of the triangle $= y$.

Then $\qquad |OP| = 1 + y$

$$\cos a = \frac{y}{2}$$

$$2\cos a = x$$

$\therefore \qquad |OP| = 1 + 2\cos a$

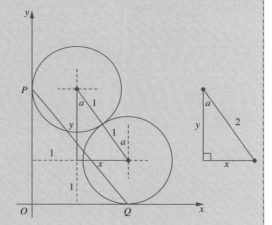

Use Pythagoras' theorem:

$$d^2 = (1 + 2\sin a)^2 + (1 + 2\cos a)^2$$
$$= 1 + 4\sin a + 4\sin^2 a + 1 + 4\cos a + 4\cos^2 a$$
$$= 2 + 4\sin a + 4\cos a + 4\sin^2 a + 4\cos^2 a$$
$$= 2 + 4\sin a + 4\cos a + 4\,(\sin^2 a + 4\cos^2 a)$$
$$= 2 + 4\sin a + 4\cos a + 4(1)$$
$$= 2 + 4\sin a + 4\cos a + 4$$
$$= 6 + 4\sin a + 4\cos a$$
$$\therefore d^2 = 6 + 4\cos a + 4\sin a$$

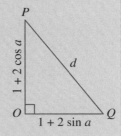

(iii) If $a = \dfrac{\pi}{4}$:

$|OQ| = 1 + 2 \sin a$

$|OQ| = 1 + 2 \sin \dfrac{\pi}{4} \quad \Rightarrow \quad |OQ| = 1 + 2\left(\dfrac{\sqrt{2}}{2}\right) \quad \Rightarrow \quad |OQ| = 1 + \sqrt{2}$

If $a = \dfrac{\pi}{4}$:

$|OP| = 1 + 2 \cos a$

$|OP| = 1 + 2 \cos \dfrac{\pi}{4} \quad \Rightarrow \quad |OP| = 1 + 2\left(\dfrac{\sqrt{2}}{2}\right) \quad \Rightarrow \quad |OP| = 1 + \sqrt{2}$

Area $\triangle POQ = \dfrac{1}{2}\,|OQ| \times |OP|$

$\qquad = \dfrac{1}{2}\,(1 + \sqrt{2}) \times (1 + \sqrt{2})$

$\qquad = \dfrac{1}{2}\,(1 + 2\sqrt{2} + 2)$

$\qquad = \dfrac{1}{2}\,(3 + 2\sqrt{2})$

$\therefore$ Area $\triangle POQ = \dfrac{3}{2} + \sqrt{2}$ square units

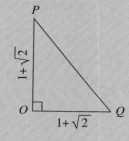

aims

- ☐ To graph any trigonometrical function of the form $a + b \sin c\theta$ and $a + b \cos c\theta$ and $b \tan c\theta$ for $a, b, c \in \mathbb{R}$
- ☐ To identify a trigonometrical graph, its period and range
- ☐ To model situations using a trigonometrical function
- ☐ To interpret graphs which model a situation
- ☐ To understand and simplify 3D situations
- ☐ To understand a compound angle and its associated formulae
- ☐ To manipulate the compound angle formulae
- ☐ To prove trigonometrical identities

Graph of trigonometric functions

The table shows values for $\sin \theta$, $\cos \theta$ and $\tan \theta$ for $0 \leq \theta \leq 2\pi$.

θ	0	$\dfrac{\pi}{4}$	$\dfrac{\pi}{2}$	$\dfrac{3\pi}{4}$	π	$\dfrac{5\pi}{4}$	$\dfrac{3\pi}{2}$	$\dfrac{7\pi}{4}$	2π
$\sin \theta$	0	0·7	1	0·7	0	−0·7	−1	−0·7	0
$\cos \theta$	1	0·7	0	−0·7	−1	−0·7	0	0·7	1
$\tan \theta$	0	1	undefined	−1	0	1	undefined	−1	0

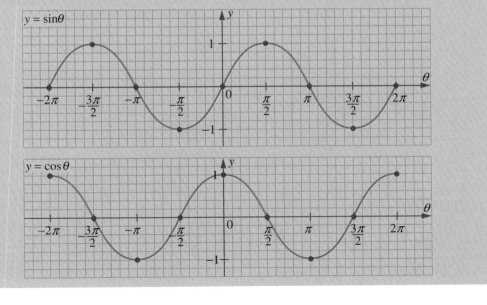

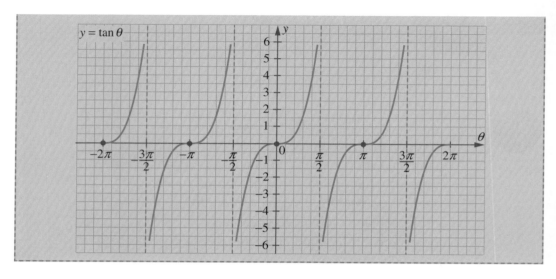

Period and range

The **period** is the minimum horizontal distance over which the graph repeats indefinitely.

The **range** is a set of values from the lowest to the highest that the function can produce.

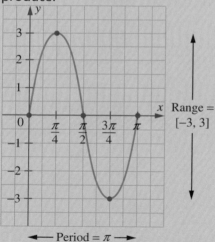

Range = [−3, 3]

Period = π

	Period	Range
sin θ	2π	[−1, 1]
cos θ	2π	[−1, 1]
tan θ	π	$\mathbb{R}$

Variations on the basic trigonometric functions:

	Period	Range
b sin cθ	$\dfrac{2\pi}{c}$	[−b, b]
b cos cθ	$\dfrac{2\pi}{c}$	[−b, b]
b tan cθ	$\dfrac{\pi}{c}$	$\mathbb{R}$

	Period	Range
a + b sin cθ	$\dfrac{2\pi}{c}$	[−b + a, b + a]
a + b cos cθ	$\dfrac{2\pi}{c}$	[−b + a, b + a]

- Sin and cos have the same values for period and range, while tan is very different.
- Multiplying the function by a value multiplies the range by the same value. For example, the range for $2 \sin \theta$ is $[-2, 2]$.
- Increasing the angle reduces the period. For example, the period for $\cos 3\theta$ is $\frac{2\pi}{3}$.
- Adding or subtracting a value to the entire function shifts the graph up or down the y-axis. For example, the range for $4 + \sin \theta$ is $[3, 5]$.

exam focus

You must be able to recognise the period, range and vertical position of a graph and use it to identify the exact trigonometric function, in the form:

$$a + b \sin c\theta, \; a + b \cos c\theta \text{ for } a, b, c \in \mathbb{R}.$$

Example

The diagram shows the graph of a function of the form $y = a \cos bx$ for $0 \le x \le 2\pi$.

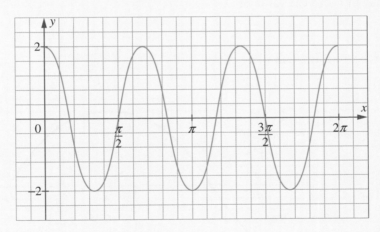

(i) What is the period and range of this function?

(ii) What is the value of a and the value of b?

Solution

(i) The range is $[-2, 2]$ from the graph.

Between 0 and 2π there are three complete U-shaped segments to this curve.

This means that the curve repeats itself three times in 2π and so the period is $\frac{2\pi}{3}$.

(ii) As the range is $[-2, 2]$ and the graph looks like the usual cosine graph, the value of a is 2.

As the graph has three repeated segments, the value of b must be 3.

The equation of the graph is $y = 2 \cos 3x$.

Example

The diagram shows part of the graph of the function $y = v \sin \left(\frac{x}{w}\right)$.

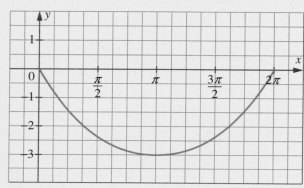

Find the value of v and the value of w.

Solution

A quick sketch of a more complete curve:

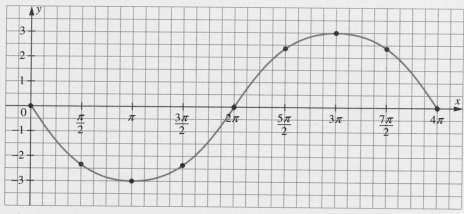

To find v, we concentrate on the range.

The graph appears to be more like $\sin x$ than $\cos x$, as it begins at $(0, 0)$. However, it is upside-down so it must be a multiple of $-\sin x$.

As the range is $[-3, 3]$, we deduce that $v = -3$.

Now to find w:

Method 1:

The period of $a \sin bx$ is $\dfrac{2\pi}{b}$.

As $v \sin \left(\dfrac{x}{w}\right) = v \sin \left(\dfrac{1}{w}x\right)$, its period should be $\dfrac{2\pi}{\frac{1}{w}} = 2w\pi$.

From our sketch, the period is 4π, so $2w\pi = 4\pi \Rightarrow w = 2$.

Method 2:

The curve takes twice as long as usual to complete its period. So instead of $\sin x$, the graph must be $v \sin \left(\dfrac{x}{2}\right)$, so $w = 2$.

Example

The diagram below shows the graph of $y = 2 \sin 2x + 1$ for $0 \le x \le \pi$.

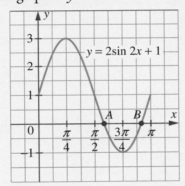

(i) Find the coordinates of A and B (as shown in the diagram) by solving an appropriate equation algebraically.

(ii) The points $(0, 2)$ and $(\pi, 0)$ are joined by a straight line, k. How many times does k intersect the given curve?

(iii) C is the point on the given graph with an x-coordinate of $\dfrac{\pi}{2}$. Investigate whether C is above, below or on the line k.

Solution

(i) A and B are on the x-axis where $y = 0$.

$$2 \sin 2x + 1 = 0$$

$$\sin 2x = -\dfrac{1}{2}$$

$$2x = \sin^{-1}\left(-\dfrac{1}{2}\right)$$

$$2x = \frac{7\pi}{6} \quad \text{or} \quad \frac{11\pi}{6} \qquad \text{(using unit circle)}$$

$$x = \frac{7\pi}{12} \quad \text{or} \quad \frac{11\pi}{12}$$

$A\left(\frac{7\pi}{12}, 0\right)$ and $B\left(\frac{11\pi}{12}, 0\right)$

(ii) Adding the line to the graph:

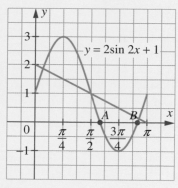

k intersects the curve 3 times

(iii) If $x = \frac{\pi}{2}$, then $y = 2\sin 2x + 1 = 2\sin 2\left(\frac{\pi}{2}\right) + 1 = 2\sin \pi + 1 = 0 + 1 = 1$.

The corresponding point on the curve is $C\left(\frac{\pi}{2}, 1\right)$.

The midpoint of the line segment joining $(0, 2)$ and $(\pi, 0)$ is also $\left(\frac{\pi}{2}, 1\right)$, so C is on the line k.

You could also find the equation of the line joining $(0, 2)$ and $(\pi, 0)$ and then determine whether or not C is on this line by substituting its coordinates in for x and y.

The function $f : x \rightarrow 3\sin(2x)$ is defined for $x \in \mathbb{R}$.

(i) Complete the table.

x	0	$\frac{\pi}{4}$	$\frac{\pi}{2}$	$\frac{3\pi}{4}$	π
$2x$					
$\sin(2x)$					
$3\sin(2x)$					

(ii) Draw the graph of $y = f(x)$ in the domain $0 \le x \le \pi$, $x \in \mathbb{R}$.

(iii) Write down the period and range of f.

Solution

(i) The table:

x	0	$\dfrac{\pi}{4}$	$\dfrac{\pi}{2}$	$\dfrac{3\pi}{4}$	π
2x	0	$\dfrac{\pi}{2}$	π	$\dfrac{3\pi}{2}$	2π
sin(2x)	0	1	0	1	0
3 sin(2x)	0	3	0	3	0

(ii) The graph:

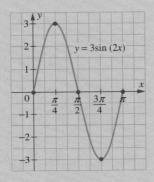

(iii) The period is π.

The range is $[-3, 3]$.

The diagram shows the graph of the function $f : x \rightarrow \sin 2x$.
The line $2y = 1$ is also shown.

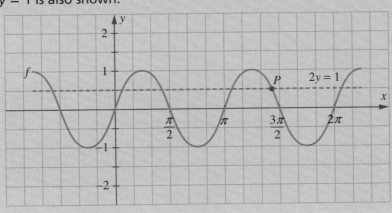

(i) On the same diagram, sketch the graphs of $g : x \rightarrow \sin x$ and $h : x \rightarrow 3 \sin 2x$. Indicate clearly which is g and which is h.

(ii) Find the coordinates of the point P in the diagram.

Solution

(i) Make sure to identify each graph. Using colour is an option. Labelling them on the left side where the graphs begin is another option.

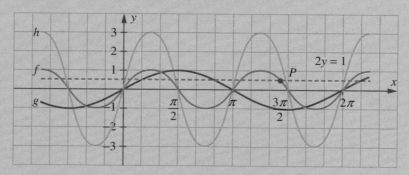

(ii) The point P is where the $2y = 1$ line intersects the $\sin 2x$ curve.

$$2y = 1 \implies y = \frac{1}{2}$$

$$\sin 2x = \frac{1}{2}$$

$$2x = \sin^{-1}\frac{1}{2}$$

$$2x = \frac{\pi}{6} \text{ or } \frac{5\pi}{6} \text{ or } \frac{13\pi}{6} \text{ or } \frac{17\pi}{6} \text{ or } \dots$$

$$x = \frac{\pi}{12} \text{ or } \frac{5\pi}{12} \text{ or } \frac{13\pi}{12} \text{ or } \frac{17\pi}{12} \text{ or } \dots$$

We need the 4th point of intersection, from the right of the y-axis, so P is $\left(\dfrac{17\pi}{12}, \dfrac{1}{2}\right)$.

(i) Solve the equation $\sin 2x = \sqrt{3} \sin x$ for $0° \leq x \leq 360°$.

(ii) The diagram shows two functions, $f(x) = 2\sqrt{3} \sin x$ and $g(x) = 2 \sin 2x$, in the domain $0° \leq x \leq 360°$. Identify which is curve A and which is curve B.

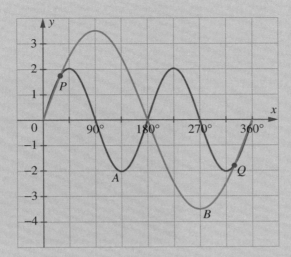

(iii) Find the coordinates of the points P and Q.

Solution

(i)
$$\sin 2x = \sqrt{3} \sin x$$

$$2 \sin x \cos x = \sqrt{3} \sin x \qquad \text{(booklet of formulae and tables page 14)}$$

$$2 \sin x \cos x - \sqrt{3} \sin x = 0$$

$$\sin x(2 \cos x - \sqrt{3}) = 0$$

$$\sin x = 0 \text{ or } 2 \cos x - \sqrt{3} = 0$$

$$\sin x = 0 \text{ or } \cos x = \frac{\sqrt{3}}{2}$$

$$x = 0°, 180°, 360° \text{ or } x = 30°, 330°$$

Do not divide all parts by $\sin x$ here, as that would eliminate some solutions. Factorise out the $\sin x$.

Five solutions: $x = 0°, 30°, 180°, 330°, 360°$.

(ii) The taller graph is a multiple of $\sin x$, so graph B must be $f(x) = 2\sqrt{3} \sin x$. The busier graph has two repeated segments within the domain of 360°, so it is a multiple of $\sin 2x$ and so graph A is $g(x) = 2 \sin 2x$.

(iii) To find the points of intersection, we let

$$2 \sin 2x = 2\sqrt{3} \sin x$$

$$\sin 2x = \sqrt{3} \sin x \qquad \text{(already solved above)}$$

By inspection, P must be $(30°, ?)$ and $Q(330°, ?)$.

$$P\colon x = 30° \Rightarrow y = 2 \sin 2(30°) = 2 \sin 60° = 2\left(\frac{\sqrt{3}}{2}\right) = \sqrt{3}$$

$$Q\colon x = 330° \Rightarrow y = 2 \sin 2(330°) = 2 \sin 660° = 2 \sin 300° = 2\left(-\frac{\sqrt{3}}{2}\right) = -\sqrt{3}$$

$$P(30°, \sqrt{3}) \text{ and } Q(330°, -\sqrt{3}) \quad \text{or} \quad P = \left(\frac{\pi}{6}, \sqrt{3}\right) \text{ and } Q\left(\frac{11\pi}{6}, -\sqrt{3}\right)$$

A local authority is analysing its water usage during a period of time in history. They discovered that it was possible to represent the approximate amount of water, $W(t)$, in millions of litres, stored in a reservoir t months after 1 May 1946 by the formula

$$W(t) = 1 \cdot 1 - \sin \frac{\pi t}{6}.$$

(i) Draw and label the sketches of the graphs of $y = \sin \frac{\pi t}{6}$ and $y = -\sin \frac{\pi t}{6}$, for $0 \le t \le 36$, on the same diagram.

(ii) On a separate diagram and using the same scale on the t-axis as you used in part (i), draw a sketch of the graph of $W(t) = 1 \cdot 1 - \sin \frac{\pi t}{6}$.

(iii) With further research, the local authority discovered that on 1 April 1948, there was a serious fire in the area. This fire required an extra $\frac{1}{4}$ million litres of water from the reservoir to bring the fire under control.

Assuming that the previous trend continued and that water rationing was not imposed to compensate for the loss of this additional water, when did the reservoir run dry?

Solution

(i) Sketches:

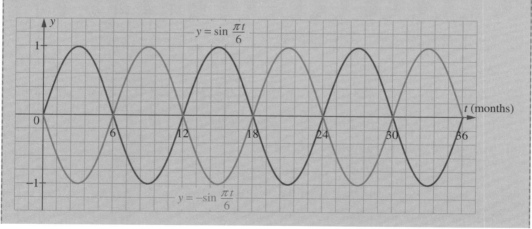

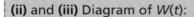

(ii) and **(iii)** Diagram of $W(t)$:

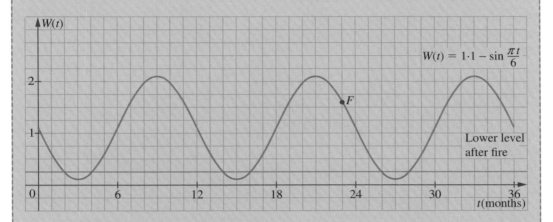

$$W(t) = 1 \cdot 1 - \sin \frac{\pi t}{6}$$

Lower level after fire

The red curve shows that the water will go to a very low level during the summer months of each year.

The fire occurred when $t = 23$ (23 months after 1 May 1946), marked F on the diagram. Given that the fire required the use of an extra 0·25 million litres of water, if rationing was not imposed, the reservoir would be empty at the time when it would usually have had 0·25 million litres in reserve.

The green line on the diagram shows the lower level raised to 0·25 million litres to account for this loss in water.

After $t = 23$ months, the red curve first hits this green line at $t = 26$, so the reservoir is most likely to have run dry when $t = 26$, 1 July 1948.

3D problems

Some trigonometrical problems will involve a three-dimensional situation. In these questions, it is a good idea to break the diagram up into small flat pieces.

Many 3D problems will involve right angles. This is because a vertical plane (e.g. a wall) meets a horizontal plane (e.g. the ground) at right angles.

Example

[SP] and [TQ] are vertical poles, each of height 10 m.
P, Q and R are points on level ground.
Two wires of equal length join S and T to
R, i.e. $|SR| = |TR|$.

If $|PR| = 8$ m and $|\angle PRQ| = 120°$, calculate:

(i) $|SR|$ in the form $c\sqrt{d}$, where d is prime
(ii) $|PQ|$ in the form $a\sqrt{b}$, where b is prime
(iii) $|\angle SRT|$ to the nearest degree

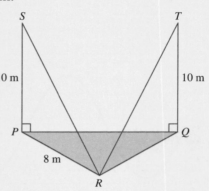

Solution

Redraw the triangles separately.

(i)
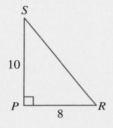

Using Pythagoras' theorem:
$$|SR|^2 = |SP|^2 + |PR|^2$$
$$= 10^2 + 8^2$$
$$|SR|^2 = 164$$
$$|SR| = \sqrt{164}$$
$$|SR| = 2\sqrt{41}$$

(ii) $|SP| = |TQ| = 10$ m (given)
$|\angle SPR| = |\angle TQR| = 90°$
$|SR| = |TR|$ (given)
∴ $\triangle SPR \equiv \triangle TQR$ (RHS)
∴ $|PR| = |QR| = 8$ m

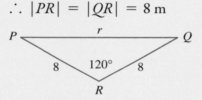

Let $|PQ| = r$.

Using the cosine rule:
$$r^2 = p^2 + q^2 - 2pq \cos R$$
$$r^2 = 8^2 + 8^2 - 2(8)(8) \cos 120°$$
$$r^2 = 192$$
$$r = \sqrt{192} = 8\sqrt{3}$$

(iii) $r^2 = s^2 + t^2 - 2st \cos R$
$$(8\sqrt{3})^2 = (2\sqrt{41})^2 + (2\sqrt{41})^2 - 2(2\sqrt{41})(2\sqrt{41}) \cos R$$
$$192 = 164 + 164 - 328 \cos R$$
$$328 \cos R = 136$$
$$\cos R = \frac{136}{328} = \frac{17}{41}$$
$$R = \cos^{-1}\frac{17}{41} = 65·50372095°$$
$$|\angle SRT| = 66° \text{ to the nearest degree}$$

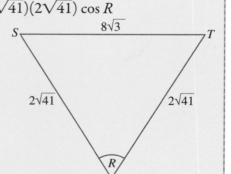

If you can imagine walking around the object(s), it will give you a better understanding of the situation. During the exam, you could use your set square to model a situation.

Example

The diagram shows a crystal pyramid of rectangular base 12 mm by 7 mm and slant height of 28 mm.

Calculate the vertical height of the crystal, correct to one decimal place.

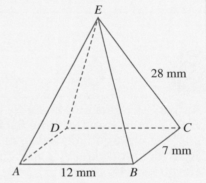

Solution

Redraw the diagram, marking in the vertical height with base point P.

Construct a right-angled triangle involving the vertical height and the slant height.

The third side of the triangle is along the base of the triangle, from the centre of the rectangular base to one of the corners.

By considering the rectangular base, we can calculate $|AC|$ and therefore the base of our new triangle.

$$|AC|^2 = 12^2 + 7^2$$
$$|AC|^2 = 193$$
$$|AC| = \sqrt{193}$$
$$\therefore |PC| = \frac{\sqrt{193}}{2}$$

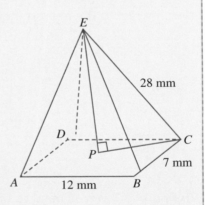

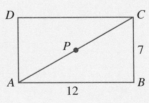

Back to the triangle EPC to find $|EP|$, the vertical height.

$$|EP|^2 + \left(\frac{\sqrt{193}}{2}\right)^2 = 28^2$$

$$|EP|^2 = 28^2 - \left(\frac{\sqrt{193}}{2}\right)^2$$

$$|EP|^2 = \frac{2{,}943}{4}$$

$$\therefore |EP| = \frac{3\sqrt{327}}{2} = 27{\cdot}12471198$$

Thus, the vertical height is 27·1 mm, correct to one decimal place.

A river flows due east and a tower $[BT]$ stands on its left bank. From a point P on the same bank as the tower, the angle of elevation of the top of the tower, T, is 55°. From a point Q directly opposite to P, the angle of elevation is 46°.

If the height of the tower is 40 m, find the width of the river, correct to the nearest metre.

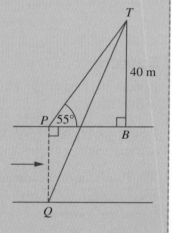

Solution
To find $|PQ|$, we will need to find information about $\triangle PQT$.

1. In $\triangle PTB$:

$$\sin 55° = \frac{40}{|PT|}$$

$$|PT| = \frac{40}{\sin 55°}$$

$$= 48{\cdot}83098355$$

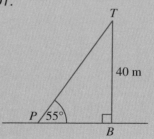

2. In $\triangle QTB$:

$$\sin 46° = \frac{40}{|QT|}$$

$$|QT| = \frac{40}{\sin 46°}$$

$$= 55 \cdot 60654364$$

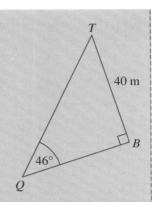

40 m

46°

3. Finally, $\triangle PQT$ is right-angled because PQ is horizontal and PT is in a vertical plane.

$$|QT|^2 = |PT|^2 + |PQ|^2$$

$$(55\cdot60654)^2 = (48\cdot83098)^2 + |PQ|^2$$

$$3,092\cdot087 = 2,384\cdot465 + |PQ|^2$$

$$707\cdot622 = |PQ|^2$$

$$26\cdot6 \text{ m} = |PQ|$$

Thus, the width of the river is 26·6 m.

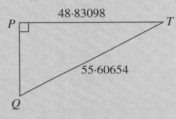

48·83098

55·60654

exam Q

QRST is a vertical rectangular wall of height h on level ground. P is a point on the ground in front of the wall. The angle of elevation of R from P is θ and the angle of elevation of S from P is 2θ.

$|PQ| = 3|PT|$.

Find θ.

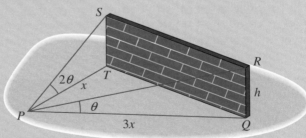

Solution

Using the nearer triangle, we find a relationship between θ, x and h.

$$\tan \theta = \frac{h}{3x}$$

$$3x \tan \theta = h$$

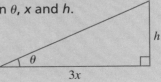

h

θ

$3x$

Using the farther triangle, we find another relationship between θ, x and h.

$$\tan 2\theta = \frac{h}{x}$$

$$x \tan 2\theta = h$$

$3x \tan \theta = x \tan 2\theta$ (as both equal h)

$3 \tan \theta = \tan 2\theta$ (divide both sides by non-zero x)

$3 \tan \theta = \dfrac{2 \tan \theta}{1 - \tan^2 \theta}$ (from formula $\tan 2\theta = \frac{2 \tan \theta}{1 - \tan^2 \theta}$)

$3t = \dfrac{2t}{1 - t^2}$ (abbreviating $\tan \theta$ as t)

$3t(1 - t^2) = 2t$

$3t - 3t^3 - 2t = 0$

$t - 3t^3 = 0$

$3t^3 - t = 0$

$t(3t^2 - 1) = 0$

$t = 0$ or $t = \dfrac{1}{\sqrt{3}}$ or $t = -\dfrac{1}{\sqrt{3}}$

$\tan \theta = 0$ or $\tan \theta = \dfrac{1}{\sqrt{3}}$ or $\tan \theta = -\dfrac{1}{\sqrt{3}}$

Rejecting 0 (θ cannot be 0) and $-\frac{1}{\sqrt{3}}$ (θ cannot be obtuse), we are left with $\tan \theta = \frac{1}{\sqrt{3}} \Rightarrow \theta = 60°$ or $\frac{\pi}{6}$ rads.

exam
Q

A tower that is part of a hotel has a square base of side 4 metres and a roof in the form of a pyramid. The owners plan to cover the roof with copper. To find the amount of copper needed, they need to know the total area of the roof. A surveyor stands 10 metres from the tower, measured horizontally, and makes observations of angles of elevation from the point O as follows:

The angle of elevation of the top of the roof is 46°.

The angle of elevation of the closest point at the bottom of the roof is 42°.

The angle of depression of the closest point at the bottom of the tower is 9°.

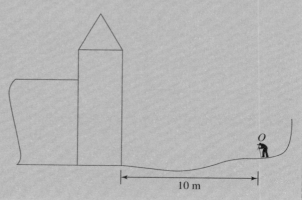

(i) Find the vertical height of the roof.

(ii) Find the total area of the roof.

(iii) If all of the angles observed are subject to a possible error of ±1°, find the range of possible areas for the roof.

Solution

(i) In the solid triangle:

$$\tan 42° = \frac{y}{10}$$

$$y = 10 \tan 42°$$

$$y = 9·004$$

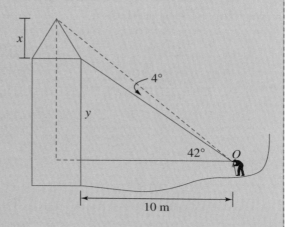

In the dashed triangle:

$$\tan 46° = \frac{x + y}{12}$$

$$x + y = 12 \tan 46$$

$$x = 12·426 - 9·004$$

$$= 3·42$$

∴ Height of roof = 3·42 m

(ii) $$L = \sqrt{3·42^2 + 2^2}$$

$$L = 3·964$$

$$\text{Area} = 4\left(\frac{1}{2}(4)(3·964)\right) = 31·71 \text{ m}^2$$

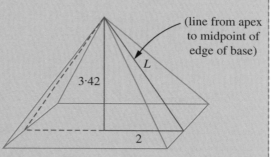

(line from apex to midpoint of edge of base)

(iii) Maximum possible area of roof given by:

Angle of elevation of bottom = 41°

Angle of elevation of top = 47°

∴ Height = 12 tan 47° − 10 tan 41° = 4·18 m

$$x = \sqrt{4·18^2 + 2^2} = 4·634 \text{ m}$$

Area = 37·07 m²

Minimum possible area of roof given by:

Angle of elevation of bottom = 43°

Angle of elevation of top = 45°

∴ Height = 12 tan 45° − 10 tan 43° = 2·675 m

$$x = \sqrt{2·675^2 + 2^2} = 3·34 \text{ m}$$

Area = 26·72 m²

26·72 m² ≤ area of roof ≤ 37·07 m²

key point

The 9° angle of depression was unnecessary information. The ground does not have to be level because the surveyor's line of sight is horizontal and so forms the base of a right-angled triangle.

Trigonometric formulae

You must be able to apply the trigonometric formulae 1–24, listed in the table below. These formulae are in your booklet of formulae and tables.

Of these formulae, you must be able to derive the trigonometric formulae 1, 2, 3, 4, 5, 6, 7 and 9, which are **marked with an asterisk (*)** in the table below. These derivations are in New Concise Project Maths 4.

1.* $\cos^2A + \sin^2A = 1$	13. $\cos 2A = \dfrac{1 - \tan^2A}{1 + \tan^2A}$
2.* Sine formula: $\dfrac{a}{\sin A} = \dfrac{b}{\sin B} = \dfrac{c}{\sin C}$	14. $\tan 2A = \dfrac{2 \tan A}{1 - \tan^2A}$
3.* Cosine formula: $a^2 = b^2 + c^2 - 2bc \cos A$	15. $\cos^2A = \frac{1}{2}(1 + \cos 2A)$
4.* $\cos (A - B) = \cos A \cos B + \sin A \sin B$	16. $\sin^2A = \frac{1}{2}(1 - \cos 2A)$
5.* $\cos (A + B) = \cos A \cos B - \sin A \sin B$	17. $2 \cos A \cos B = \cos (A + B) + \cos (A - B)$
6.* $\cos 2A = \cos^2A - \sin^2A$	18. $2 \sin A \cos B = \sin (A + B) + \sin (A - B)$
7.* $\sin (A + B) = \sin A \cos B + \cos A \sin B$	19. $2 \sin A \sin B = \cos (A - B) - \cos (A + B)$
8. $\sin (A - B) = \sin A \cos B - \cos A \sin B$	20. $2 \cos A \sin B = \sin (A + B) - \sin (A - B)$
9.* $\tan(A + B) = \dfrac{\tan A + \tan B}{1 - \tan A \tan B}$	21. $\cos A + \cos B = 2 \cos\dfrac{A + B}{2}\cos\dfrac{A - B}{2}$
10. $\tan(A - B) = \dfrac{\tan A - \tan B}{1 + \tan A \tan B}$	22. $\cos A - \cos B = -2 \sin\dfrac{A + B}{2}\sin\dfrac{A - B}{2}$
11. $\sin 2A = 2 \sin A \cos A$	23. $\sin A + \sin B = 2 \sin\dfrac{A + B}{2}\cos\dfrac{A - B}{2}$
12. $\sin 2A = \dfrac{2 \tan A}{1 + \tan^2A}$	24. $\sin A - \sin B = 2 \cos\dfrac{A + B}{2}\sin\dfrac{A - B}{2}$

Compound angles

This deals will angles such as $A + B$ and $2B$. There are many formulae available to convert from compound angles to single angles.

Example

(i) Express cos 75° in surd form and, hence, cos 255°.

(ii) Express the following in surd form: (a) $\tan\left(-\dfrac{7\pi}{12}\right)$ (b) sin 195°.

Solution

First express each angle as a combination of 30°, 45° or 60° and then use the compound angle formulae from the booklet of formulae and tables, pages 14 and 15.

(i) $\cos 75°$

$= \cos(45° + 30°)$

$= \cos 45° \cos 30° - \sin 45° \sin 30°$

$= \dfrac{1}{\sqrt{2}} \times \dfrac{\sqrt{3}}{2} - \dfrac{1}{\sqrt{2}} \times \dfrac{1}{2}$

$= \dfrac{\sqrt{3}}{2\sqrt{2}} - \dfrac{1}{2\sqrt{2}} = \dfrac{\sqrt{3} - 1}{2\sqrt{2}}$

$= \dfrac{\sqrt{6} - \sqrt{2}}{4}$

$\cos 255°$

$= -\cos 75°$

$= -\dfrac{\sqrt{3} - 1}{2\sqrt{2}}$

$= \dfrac{1 - \sqrt{3}}{2\sqrt{2}}$

$= \dfrac{\sqrt{2} - \sqrt{6}}{4}$

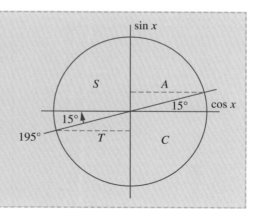

(ii) (a) $\tan\left(-\dfrac{7\pi}{12}\right) = \tan(-105°) = -\tan 105°$

$= -\tan(60° + 45°)$

$= -\dfrac{\tan 60° + \tan 45°}{1 - \tan 60° \tan 45°}$

$= -\dfrac{\sqrt{3} + 1}{1 - \sqrt{3}(1)} = -\dfrac{\sqrt{3} + 1}{1 - \sqrt{3}} = \dfrac{\sqrt{3} + 1}{\sqrt{3} - 1} = 2 + \sqrt{3}$

(b) $\sin 195° = -\sin 15°$

$= -\sin(45° - 30°)$

$= -(\sin 45° \cos 30° - \cos 45° \sin 30°)$

$= -\left(\dfrac{1}{\sqrt{2}} \times \dfrac{\sqrt{3}}{2} - \dfrac{1}{\sqrt{2}} \times \dfrac{1}{2}\right)$

$= -\left(\dfrac{\sqrt{3} - 1}{2\sqrt{2}}\right) = \dfrac{1 - \sqrt{3}}{2\sqrt{2}} = \dfrac{\sqrt{2} - \sqrt{6}}{4}$

key point

You need to be very familiar with the unit circle and be able to manipulate it to find the values you need.

In the last example, **(ii) (b)**, the value of 195° on the sine axis is the same value as 15° on the sine axis, but on the negative side of the sine axis. Therefore, $\sin 195° = -\sin 15°$.

Example

(i) If $\tan A = \dfrac{2}{3}$, evaluate $\sin 2A$, giving your answer in the form $\dfrac{a}{b}$, $a, b \in N$.

(ii) If $\cos 2A = \dfrac{1}{49}$, find the two values of $\cos A$ without using tables or a calculator.

(iii) If $\cos 2A = \dfrac{12}{13}$, find the two possible values of $\tan A$.

Solution

(i) **Method 1**

Given: $\tan A = \dfrac{2}{3}$

$\Rightarrow \sin A = \dfrac{2}{\sqrt{13}}$ and $\cos A = \dfrac{3}{\sqrt{13}}$

$\sin 2A = 2 \sin A \cos A = 2 \times \dfrac{2}{\sqrt{13}} \times \dfrac{3}{\sqrt{13}} = \dfrac{12}{13}$

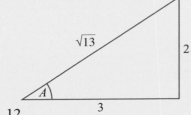

(i) **Method 2**

Given: $\tan A = \dfrac{2}{3}$

$\sin 2A = \dfrac{2 \tan A}{1 + \tan^2 A}$

$= \dfrac{2\left(\dfrac{2}{3}\right)}{1 + \left(\dfrac{2}{3}\right)^2}$

$= \dfrac{\dfrac{4}{3}}{1 + \dfrac{4}{9}} = \dfrac{12}{13}$

Remember, there can often be more than one way to solve a problem. If you try several different methods in the exam, **never erase or Tipp-Ex any of your attempts.**

All attempts will be corrected by the examiner.

(ii) Given: $\cos 2A = \dfrac{1}{49}$

$2\cos^2 A - 1 = \dfrac{1}{49}$

$2\cos^2 A = \dfrac{1}{49} + 1$

$2\cos^2 A = \dfrac{50}{49}$

$\cos^2 A = \dfrac{25}{49}$

$\cos A = \pm\dfrac{5}{7}$

(iii) Given: $\cos 2A = \dfrac{12}{13}$

$\dfrac{1 - \tan^2 A}{1 + \tan^2 A} = \dfrac{12}{13}$

$12 + 12\tan^2 A = 13 - 13\tan^2 A$

$25\tan^2 A = 1$

$\tan^2 A = \dfrac{1}{25}$

$\tan A = \pm\dfrac{1}{5}$

If $\sin \alpha = \dfrac{5}{13}$ and $\cos \beta = \dfrac{4}{5}$, $0 < \alpha < \dfrac{\pi}{2}$, $0 < \beta < \dfrac{\pi}{2}$, express

$\sin(\alpha + \beta)$ in the form $\dfrac{a}{b}$, $a, b \in N$.

Hence or otherwise, show that $\cos(45° - \alpha - \beta) = \dfrac{89\sqrt{2}}{130}$.

Solution

We represent each given angle with a right-angled triangle and use Pythagoras' theorem to find the third side and the other ratios.

Given: $\sin \alpha = \dfrac{5}{13}$

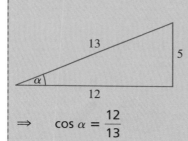

$\Rightarrow \quad \cos \alpha = \dfrac{12}{13}$

Given: $\cos \beta = \dfrac{4}{5}$

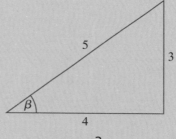

$\Rightarrow \quad \sin \beta = \dfrac{3}{5}$

$$\sin(\alpha + \beta) = \sin \alpha \cos \beta + \cos \alpha \sin \beta$$
$$= \dfrac{5}{13} \times \dfrac{4}{5} + \dfrac{12}{13} \times \dfrac{3}{5} = \dfrac{20}{65} + \dfrac{36}{65} = \dfrac{56}{65}$$

$$\cos(45° - \alpha - \beta) = \cos[45° - (\alpha + \beta)]$$
$$= \cos 45° \cos(\alpha + \beta) + \sin 45° \sin(\alpha + \beta)$$
$$= \cos 45° [\cos \alpha \cos \beta - \sin \alpha \sin \beta] + \sin 45° \sin(\alpha + \beta)$$
$$= \dfrac{1}{\sqrt{2}}\left[\dfrac{12}{13} \times \dfrac{4}{5} - \dfrac{5}{13} \times \dfrac{3}{5}\right] + \dfrac{1}{\sqrt{2}} \times \dfrac{56}{65}$$
$$= \dfrac{1}{\sqrt{2}} \times \dfrac{33}{65} + \dfrac{1}{\sqrt{2}} \times \dfrac{56}{65}$$
$$= \dfrac{33}{65\sqrt{2}} + \dfrac{56}{65\sqrt{2}}$$
$$= \dfrac{89}{65\sqrt{2}} = \dfrac{89}{65\sqrt{2}} \times \dfrac{\sqrt{2}}{\sqrt{2}} = \dfrac{89\sqrt{2}}{65(2)} = \dfrac{89\sqrt{2}}{130}$$

exam focus

$\cos(A + B + C) =$
$\cos(A + (B + C)) =$
$\cos((A + B) + C)$ is a
very useful technique
to known.

(i) If $A + B = \dfrac{\pi}{4}$, write tan A in terms of tan B, and hence prove that $(1 + \tan A)(1 + \tan B) = 2$.

(ii) Show that $\tan 22\tfrac{1}{2}° = \sqrt{2} - 1$.

Solution

(i) $\quad A + B = \dfrac{\pi}{4}$ (given)

$\Rightarrow \quad A = \dfrac{\pi}{4} - B$

$\Rightarrow \tan A = \tan\left(\dfrac{\pi}{4} - B\right)$

$\tan A = \dfrac{\tan\dfrac{\pi}{4} - \tan B}{1 + \tan\dfrac{\pi}{4}\tan B}$

$\Rightarrow \tan A = \dfrac{1 - \tan B}{1 + \tan B}$

$\left(\text{as } \tan\dfrac{\pi}{4} = 1\right)$

$(1 + \tan A)(1 + \tan B)$

$= \left(1 + \dfrac{1 - \tan B}{1 + \tan B}\right)(1 + \tan B)$

$= \left(\dfrac{1 + \tan B + 1 - \tan B}{1 + \tan B}\right)(1 + \tan B)$

$= \left(\dfrac{2}{1 + \tan B}\right)(1 + \tan B)$

$= 2$

$\therefore \ (1 + \tan A)(1 + \tan B) = 2$

(ii) Let $A = B = 22\tfrac{1}{2}°$ (as $A + B = \dfrac{\pi}{4} = 45°$).

$\qquad (1 + \tan A)(1 + \tan B) = 2$ (from above)

$\qquad (1 + \tan 22\tfrac{1}{2}°)(1 + \tan 22\tfrac{1}{2}°) = 2$

$\qquad (1 + \tan 22\tfrac{1}{2}°)^2 = 2$

$\qquad 1 + \tan 22\tfrac{1}{2}° = \sqrt{2}$

$\qquad \tan 22\tfrac{1}{2}° = \sqrt{2} - 1$

$\tan 22\dfrac{1}{2}°$ has appeared several times on exams. Watch out for it!

Trigonometric identities

Trigonometric identities are equations which involve trigonometric functions and are true for all values of the variables.

When proving a trigonometric identity, start with the more complicated side of the equation. Then, using the trigonometric formulae from your book of tables, manipulate the expression until it equals the opposite side of the equation. **That is, take one side (e.g. RHS) and manipulate it until it equals the other side (LHS).**

Example

Prove that $\sqrt{\dfrac{1 - \cos 2A}{1 + \cos 2A}} = \tan A$.

Solution

$\sqrt{\dfrac{1 - \cos 2A}{1 + \cos 2A}} = \tan A$

$$\text{LHS} = \sqrt{\dfrac{1 - \cos 2A}{1 + \cos 2A}} \qquad (\cos 2A = \cos^2 A - \sin^2 A)$$

$$= \sqrt{\dfrac{1 - (\cos^2 A - \sin^2 A)}{1 + (\cos^2 A - \sin^2 A)}}$$

$$= \sqrt{\dfrac{(1 - \cos^2 A) + \sin^2 A}{(1 - \sin^2 A) + \cos^2 A}} \qquad (1 = \cos^2 A + \sin^2 A)$$

$$= \sqrt{\dfrac{\sin^2 A + \sin^2 A}{\cos^2 A + \cos^2 A}}$$

$$= \sqrt{\dfrac{2 \sin^2 A}{2 \cos^2 A}} \qquad \left(\dfrac{\sin A}{\cos A} = \tan A\right)$$

$$= \sqrt{\tan^2 A} = \tan A = \text{RHS}$$

(i) Prove that $\sin\left(\theta + \dfrac{\pi}{4}\right) - \cos\left(\theta + \dfrac{\pi}{4}\right) = \sqrt{2}\,\sin\theta$.

(ii) Prove that $\cos\left(\dfrac{\pi}{3} + \theta\right) + \sin\left(\dfrac{\pi}{6} + \theta\right) = \cos\theta$.

Solution

In both questions, the compound angles formulae are used:

$\sin(A + B) = \sin A \cos B + \cos A \sin B$ and $\cos(A + B) = \cos A \cos B - \sin A \sin B$

(i) $\text{LHS} = \sin\left(\theta + \dfrac{\pi}{4}\right) - \cos\left(\theta + \dfrac{\pi}{4}\right)$

$= \left(\sin\theta\cos\dfrac{\pi}{4} + \cos\theta\sin\dfrac{\pi}{4}\right) - \left(\cos\theta\cos\dfrac{\pi}{4} - \sin\theta\sin\dfrac{\pi}{4}\right)$

$= \sin\theta \times \dfrac{1}{\sqrt{2}} + \cancel{\cos\theta \times \dfrac{1}{\sqrt{2}}} - \cancel{\cos\theta \times \dfrac{1}{\sqrt{2}}} + \sin\theta \times \dfrac{1}{\sqrt{2}}$

$= 2\left(\sin\theta \times \dfrac{1}{\sqrt{2}}\right)$

$= \dfrac{2}{\sqrt{2}}\sin\theta$

$= \sqrt{2}\,\sin\theta \qquad \left(\dfrac{2}{\sqrt{2}} = \sqrt{2}\right)$

(ii) $\mathbf{LHS} = \cos\left(\dfrac{\pi}{3} + \theta\right) + \sin\left(\dfrac{\pi}{6} + \theta\right)$

$\qquad = \cos\dfrac{\pi}{3}\cos\theta - \sin\dfrac{\pi}{3}\sin\theta + \sin\dfrac{\pi}{6}\cos\theta + \cos\dfrac{\pi}{6}\sin\theta$

$\qquad = \dfrac{1}{2}\cos\theta - \dfrac{\sqrt{3}}{2}\sin\theta + \dfrac{1}{2}\cos\theta + \dfrac{\sqrt{3}}{2}\sin\theta$

$\qquad = 2 \times \dfrac{1}{2}\cos\theta = \cos\theta$

Prove that: **(i)** $\sin 2\theta = \dfrac{2\tan\theta}{1 + \tan^2\theta}$

$\qquad$ **(ii)** $\dfrac{\sin x}{1 + \cos x} = \tan\dfrac{x}{2}$

Solution

(i) $\sin 2\theta = \dfrac{2\tan\theta}{1 + \tan^2\theta}$

$\mathbf{RHS} = \dfrac{2\tan\theta}{1 + \tan^2\theta}$

$\qquad = \dfrac{2\dfrac{\sin\theta}{\cos\theta}}{1 + \dfrac{\sin^2\theta}{\cos^2\theta}}$

$\qquad = \dfrac{2\sin\theta\cos\theta}{\cos^2\theta + \sin^2\theta}$

$\qquad = \dfrac{\sin 2\theta}{1} = \sin 2\theta = \mathbf{LHS}$

(ii) $\dfrac{\sin x}{1 + \cos x} = \tan\dfrac{x}{2}$

From tables: $\sin 2A = 2\sin A\cos A$

So, $\sin x = 2\sin\dfrac{x}{2}\cos\dfrac{x}{2}$

From tables: $\cos 2A = 2\cos^2 A - 1$

So, $\cos x = 2\cos^2\dfrac{x}{2} - 1$

$\mathbf{LHS} = \dfrac{2\sin\dfrac{x}{2}\cos\dfrac{x}{2}}{1 + \left(2\cos^2\dfrac{x}{2} - 1\right)}$

$\qquad = \dfrac{2\sin\dfrac{x}{2}\cos\dfrac{x}{2}}{1 + 2\cos^2\dfrac{x}{2} - 1}$

$\qquad = \dfrac{2\sin\dfrac{x}{2}\cos\dfrac{x}{2}}{2\cos^2\dfrac{x}{2}}$

$\qquad = \dfrac{\sin\dfrac{x}{2}}{\cos\dfrac{x}{2}}$

$\qquad = \tan\dfrac{x}{2} = \mathbf{RHS}$

7 Perimeter, Area, Volume and Nets

aims

- ☐ Know where to find the relevant information in the booklet of formulae and tables
- ☐ Know how to calculate the perimeter and area of regular 2D shapes
- ☐ Know how to calculate the area of irregular shapes (i.e. apply the trapezoidal rule)
- ☐ Understand the link between integration and the trapezoidal rule
- ☐ Know how to calculate the surface areas and volumes of cuboids, cylinders, cones, spheres and compound shapes
- ☐ Know what a net is and how to draw a net
- ☐ Gain the skills to apply the above knowledge to the examination questions
- ☐ Understand that techniques learned in geometry, trigonometry, calculus and algebra sections are often required to solve area and volume questions

Perimeter and area

key point

- When using $\pi = \dfrac{22}{7}$, it is good practice to write the radius as a fraction $\left(\text{for example, } 21 = \dfrac{21}{1} \text{ or } 4.5 = \dfrac{9}{2}\right)$.

- If a question says 'give your answer in terms of π', then leave π in the answer: do not use 3.14 or $\dfrac{22}{7}$ for π.

- Modern calculators can leave your answer in terms of π. This can be very useful.

- If you are not given an approximate value for π, then you must use the value given by the calculator.

- It is vital to know the whereabouts of the relevant information in the booklet of formulae and tables.

Example

Calculate the value of $\sqrt{\dfrac{4}{3}\pi(13\cdot6)^3}$, giving the answer:

(i) Correct to two decimal places

(ii) Correct to two significant figures

(iii) Correct to the nearest whole number

(iv) Write your answer from part (iii) in the form $a \times 10^k$ where $1 \leq a < 10$ and $k \in \mathbb{Z}$.

Solution

(i) Calculator $\Rightarrow \sqrt{\dfrac{4}{3}\pi(13\cdot6)^3} = \sqrt{10{,}536\cdot71745} = 102\cdot648514$

$= 102\cdot65$ (correct to two decimal places)

(ii) $102\cdot6485141 = 100$ (correct to two significant figures)

(iii) $102\cdot6485141 = 103$ (correct to nearest whole number)

(iv) $103 = 1\cdot03 \times 100 = 1\cdot03 \times 10^2$

It is important to know what the phrases correct to

- two decimal places
- two significant figures
- the nearest integer etc.

are asking of you.

Example

The mean distance of the Earth from the sun is 149·6 million kilometres.

(i) Write the number 149·6 million in the form $a \times 10^k$ where $1 \leq a < 10$ and $k \in \mathbb{Z}$.

(ii) The Earth travels a distance of D kilometres in one day. Show that the value of D is given by the formula

$$D = \frac{2\pi \times \text{mean distance of the Earth from the sun}}{365}.$$

Calculate the value of D, giving your answer in the form $a \times 10^k$ where $1 \leq a < 10$ and $k \in \mathbb{Z}$.

Solution

(i) 149·6 million = 149,600,000 = $1·496 \times 10^8$

(ii)

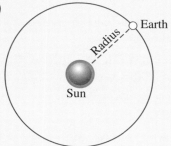

Circumference of circle
$$= 2\pi r \quad \text{(booklet of formulae and tables page 8)}$$
$$= 2\pi(1·496 \times 10^8)$$

Since there are 365 days in a year, the distance the Earth travels each day:

$$D = \frac{\text{Total distance in year}}{365} = \frac{2\pi(1·496 \times 10^8)}{365}$$

$D = 0·025752452 \times 10^8 \quad \text{(calculator)}$

$D = 2·5752452 \times 10^6 \text{ km}$

The diagram represents the frame of a photograph in the shape of a regular hexagon of side-length 30 cm.

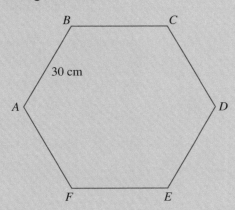

(i) Find the perimeter of the frame.

(ii) Find the area of the frame.

(iii) Hence or otherwise, derive a formula for:

    (a) the perimeter

    (b) the area of a similar hexagonal-shaped frame of side-length k cm.

Solution

(i) A hexagon has six sides, so its perimeter = 6 × 30 cm = 180 cm.

(ii)

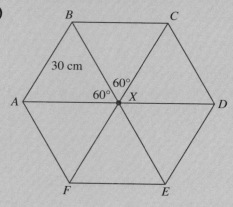

Notes:

1. All the angles at the centre, X, equal 60°.

2. $|AX| = |BX| = |CX| = |DX| = |EX| = |FX| = $ radius

△ABX is isosceles because $|AX| = |BX|$.

This means the base angles of △ABX are equal. In fact, $|\angle ABX| = |\angle BAX| = 60°$.

Hence, △ABX is equilateral, all sides = 30 cm.

$$\text{Area } \triangle ABX = \frac{1}{2}ab \sin C \quad \text{(see booklet of formulae and tables, page 9)}$$

$$= \frac{1}{2}(30)(30) \sin 60°$$

$$= 450\frac{\sqrt{3}}{2} = 225\sqrt{3} \text{ cm}^2$$

Area of frame = 6 Area △ABX = 6[225√3] = 1,350√3 cm²

(iii) (a) If each side has length k cm,

then the perimeter of the frame = 6 × k cm = 6k cm.

(b)

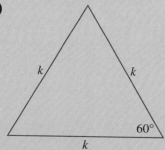

If each side has length k cm,

then area △ $= \frac{1}{2}(k)(k)\sin 60° = \frac{1}{2}k^2\frac{\sqrt{3}}{2}$.

Hence, area of frame $= 6\left[\frac{1}{2}k^2\frac{\sqrt{3}}{2}\right]$

$$= \frac{3\sqrt{3}}{2}k^2 \text{ cm}^2.$$

key point

For a more comprehensive treatment of area and perimeter, see the textbook New Concise Project Maths 5.

Trapezoidal rule

The trapezoidal rule gives a concise formula to enable us to make a good approximation of the area of an irregular shape.

Consider the diagram below.

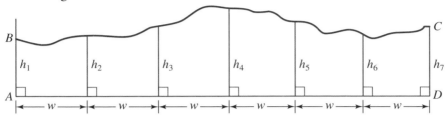

To find the area of the figure *ABCD*, do the following.

1. Divide the figure into a number of strips of equal width. (Note: The number of strips can be even or odd.)
2. Number and measure each height, *h*.
3. Use the following formula:

$$\text{Area} = \frac{w}{2}[h_1 + h_7 + 2(h_2 + h_3 + h_4 + h_5 + h_6)] \quad \text{(see formulae and tables page 12)}$$

$$\text{Area} = \frac{\text{Strip width}}{2} [\text{first height} + \text{last height} + 2(\text{sum of all remaining heights})]$$

- The greater the number of strips taken, the greater the accuracy.
- The trapezoidal rule lends itself very well to real-life in-context questions, e.g. area of a lake or area under a curve.

Example

A sketch of a piece of land is shown. Using the trapezoidal rule, the area of the piece of land is estimated to be 141 m². Calculate the value of *k*.

All units given in the diagram are in metres.

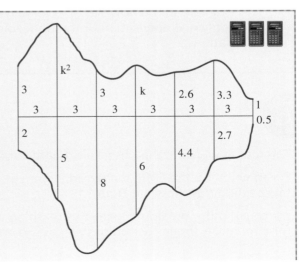

Solution

Width $= w = 3$

$h_1 = 5$

$h_2 = k^2 + 5$ $h_5 = 7$

$h_3 = 11$ $h_6 = 6$

$h_4 = k + 6$ $h_7 = 1{\cdot}5$

Equation given in disguise:

$$\text{Area} = \frac{w}{2}[h_1 + h_7 + 2(h_2 + h_3 + h_4 + h_5 + h_6)]$$

$$141 = \frac{3}{2}[5 + 1{\cdot}5 + 2(k^2 + 5 + 11 + k + 6 + 7 + 6)]$$

$$282 = 3[6{\cdot}5 + 2(k^2 + k + 35)] \qquad \text{(multiply both sides by 2)}$$

$$282 = 19{\cdot}5 + 6k^2 + 6k + 210$$

$$0 = 6k^2 + 6k - 52{\cdot}5$$

$$0 = 12k^2 + 12k - 105 \qquad \text{(multiply both sides by 2)}$$

$$0 = 4k^2 + 4k - 35$$

$$0 = (2k + 7)(2k - 5)$$

$$\therefore\ 2k + 7 = 0 \quad \text{or} \quad 2k - 5 = 0$$

$$k = -\frac{7}{2} \quad \text{or} \quad k = \frac{5}{2}$$

Reject   Answer

key point

This example shows how we can merge two irregular shapes together and apply one application of the trapezoidal rule (instead of two applications).

exam Q

The rate at which flashbulbs give off light varies during the flash.

For some bulbs, the light, measured in lumens, reaches a peak and fades quickly, as shown in Figure 1.

For other bulbs, the light, instead of reaching a peak, stays at a moderate level for a relatively longer period of time, as shown in Figure 2.

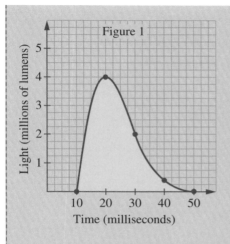

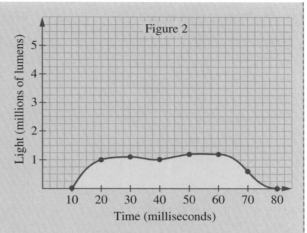

To calculate how much light reaches the film in a camera, we must know when the shutter opens and closes. A typical shutter opens after 10 milliseconds and closes approximately 60 milliseconds after the button is pressed.

The amount, A, in lumen–milliseconds of light emitted by the flash bulb is given by the shaded area under the curve.

Use the trapezoidal rule and the numerical data from Figure 1 and Figure 2 to estimate A for each of the given bulbs. State which bulb gets more light to the film. Justify your answer.

Solution

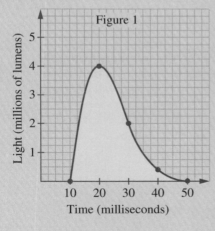

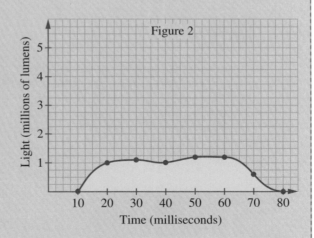

The question gives no instruction/suggestion for the interval widths. Here, each interval width is taken as 10 milliseconds. An interval width of 5 milliseconds would give a more accurate answer.

Given values:

Width = w = 10

$h_1 = 0$

$h_2 = 4$

$h_3 = 2$

$h_4 = 0\cdot4$

$h_5 = 0$

Area = $\dfrac{w}{2}[h_1 + h_5 + 2(h_2 + h_3 + h_4)]$

Area = $\dfrac{10}{2}[0 + 0 + 2(4 + 2 + 0\cdot4)]$

Area = $5[0 + 12\cdot8]$

Area = 64 lumen–milliseconds

Given values:

Width = w = 10

$h_1 = 0$

$h_2 = 1$

$h_3 = 1\cdot1$

$h_4 = 1$

$h_5 = 1\cdot2$

$h_6 = 1\cdot2$

$h_7 = 0\cdot6$

$h_8 = 0$

Area = $\dfrac{w}{2}[h_1 + h_8 + 2(h_2 + h_3 + h_4 + h_5 + h_6 + h_7)]$

Area = $\dfrac{10}{2}[0 + 0 + 2(1 + 1\cdot1 + 1 + 1\cdot2 + 1\cdot2 + 0\cdot6)]$

Area = $5[0 + 12\cdot2]$

Area = 61 lumen–milliseconds

Hence, we conclude the bulb from Figure 1 gets more light to the film.

key point

The flash bulb problem is a question where you use the numbers from the graphs and the paragraphs of text to solve the question. Do not be thrown by the language, (e.g. lumens), but look for the numbers that will be useful.

A part of the function $f(x) = e^{-x}$ is shown in the diagram.

(i) Complete the following table, giving each value for e^{-x} correct to one decimal place.

x	−3	−2	−1	0	1
$f(x) = e^{-x}$					

(ii) Hence, use the trapezoidal rule with four equal strips to estimate the area under the curve $f(x) = e^{-x}$ in the domain $-3 \leq x \leq 1$ where $x \in \mathbb{R}$.

(iii) Find the area under the curve by evaluating

$$\int_{-3}^{1} e^{-x}dx \text{ correct to one decimal place}$$

(see the chapter on integration in the LSMS Paper 1 book).

(iv) Find the error between (ii) and (iii).

(v) Given the same domain for $f(x) = e^{-x}$ from $-3 \leq x \leq 1$ where $x \in \mathbb{R}$ is divided into five strips of equal width, write down your estimate for the area without doing any calculations. Justify your answer.

Solution

(i)

x	−3	−2	−1	0	1
$f(x) = e^{-x}$	20·1	7·4	2·7	1	0·4

e.g. $e^{-(-3)} = 20 \cdot 0855 \ldots$ on calculator

$e^0 = 1$

(ii)

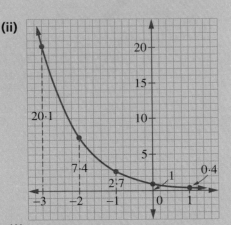

width $= w = 1$

$h_1 = 20 \cdot 1$

$h_2 = 7 \cdot 4$

$h_3 = 2 \cdot 7$

$h_4 = 1$

$h_5 = 0 \cdot 4$

Area $= \dfrac{w}{2}[h_1 + h_5 + 2(h_2 + h_3 + h_4)]$

$= \dfrac{1}{2}[20 \cdot 1 + 0 \cdot 4 + 2(7 \cdot 4 + 2 \cdot 7 + 1)]$

$= \dfrac{1}{2}[20 \cdot 5 + 22 \cdot 2]$

$= 21 \cdot 35$ square units

(iii)

key point

This solution requires a skill from integral calculus.

$$\int_{-3}^{1} e^{-x}dx = \left[-e^{-x}\right]_{-3}^{1}$$ (see integral calculus in LSMS LC HL Paper 1)

$$= -e^{-1} - (-e^{+3})$$
$$= -0.367879 + 20.0855$$
$$= 19.7176$$
$$= 19.7 \text{ square units}$$

(iv) Error between **(ii)** and **(iii)** given by $21.35 - 19.7 = 1.65$ square units.

(v) The trapezoidal rule using five strips of equal width gives a more accurate answer than using four strips of equal width, as in **(ii)**.

$$\int_{-3}^{1} e^{-x}dx = 19.7 \text{ gives a precise answer correct to one decimal place.}$$

Hence, a reasonable estimate for area using five equal strips could be 20.5 square units, or any value between answer **(ii)** and answer **(iii)**.

exam focus

- This example links area by integration and area by trapezoidal rule. Together, they form an excellent exam question.
- It is important to remember that integration gives the exact area under the curve, while the trapezoidal rule gives an approximation of the area under the curve.

Volume of cuboids, cylinders, cones and spheres

Example

Four identical spheres fit exactly into
a cuboid, the plan of which is shown
in the diagram. Given $|AC| = 6\sqrt{2}$ m,
find:

(i) The radius of a sphere
(ii) The volume of the space in the
cuboid not occupied by the spheres,
in the form $p - q\pi$ where p and
$q \in \mathbb{N}$

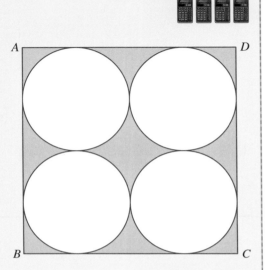

Solution

(i)

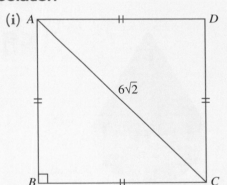

Let $x =$ the length of each side of square.

From Pythagoras, we write:

$$|AC|^2 = |AB|^2 + |BC|^2$$
$$(6\sqrt{2})^2 = x^2 + x^2$$
$$72 = 2x^2$$
$$36 = x^2$$
$$6 = x$$

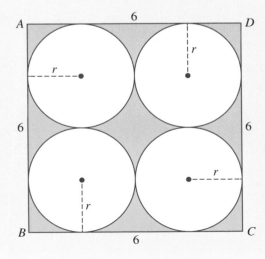

$\therefore$ Radius $= r = \dfrac{6}{4} = \dfrac{3}{2}$ m

(ii) Volume of cuboid = $l \times b \times h$

$\quad = 6 \times 6 \times 2r$

$\quad = 6 \times 6 \times 2\left(\dfrac{3}{2}\right)$

$\quad = 108$ m^3

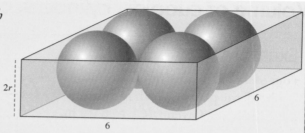

Volume of 4 spheres $= 4\left(\dfrac{4}{3}\pi r^3\right)$ (see booklet of formulae and tables page 10)

$\quad\quad = \dfrac{16}{3}\pi\left(\dfrac{3}{2}\right)^3 = \dfrac{16}{3}\pi\left(\dfrac{27}{8}\right) = 18\pi$ m^3

Volume of cuboid not occupied by spheres $= (108 - 18\pi)$ m^3.

exam Q

A buoy is made up of a cone of height h metres and a radius of 3 metres surmounted on a hemisphere. The cone is to be painted red and the hemisphere green.

Given the ratio of the red painted area to the green painted area is 5 : 6, find the slant height, l, of the cone.

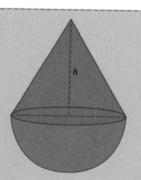

Solution

$$\frac{\text{Area red paint (cone)}}{\text{Area green paint (hemisphere)}} = \frac{5}{6}$$

$$\frac{\text{Curved surface cone}}{\text{Curved surface hemisphere}} = \frac{\pi r l}{2\pi r^2} = \frac{5}{6}$$

$$\frac{l}{2r} = \frac{5}{6}$$

Substitute $r = 3$ to get

$$\frac{l}{6} = \frac{5}{6} \Rightarrow l = 5 \text{ m}$$

A solid cone has a slant height of $2\sqrt{13}$ cm.

(i) Express r^2 in terms of h, where r is the radius and h is the vertical height of the cone.

(ii) If the volume of the cone is found to be 32π cm^3, calculate the height, h, where $h \in \mathbb{N}$ and $h < 6$.

Solution

(i)

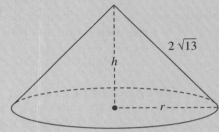

$$l^2 = h^2 + r^2 \quad \text{(Pythagoras' theorem)}$$
$$(2\sqrt{13})^2 = h^2 + r^2$$
$$52 = h^2 + r^2$$
$$52 - h^2 = r^2$$

(ii) Volume of cone $= \dfrac{1}{3}\pi r^2 h$ (see booklet of formulae and tables page 10)

$$32\pi = \frac{1}{3}\pi(52 - h^2)h \quad \text{since from (i) } r^2 = 52 - h^2$$
$$96 = 52h - h^3$$
$$h^3 - 52h + 96 = 0$$

- To solve a cubic equation, we usually have to guess a solution.
- The exam syllabus promises at least one solution in a cubic equation is a factor of the constant term.

Here we consider $h = \pm 1, \pm 2, \pm 3, \pm 4$ because $h < 6$ in the question and h will divide into 96, the constant term in our cubic equation. In addition, height h cannot be negative.

By 'trial and improvement', we find $h = 2$.

Substituting $h = 2$ into $\quad h^3 - 52h + 96 = 0$

to get $\quad (2)^3 - 52(2) + 96 = 0$

$$8 - 104 + 96 = 0$$

$\therefore h = 2$ is the solution.

(i) In Turlough Hill, a pumped storage electric power station, water issues from a cylindrical pipe of internal diameter 2·4 m at a rate of 29,000 *l* per second. At what speed is the water flowing through the pipe?

Give your answers:

(a) in m/sec correct to one decimal place

(b) in km/h correct to the nearest km.

(ii) Hence or otherwise, if the diameter of the pipe was 1·2 m, find, correct to one decimal place, the new speed of the water in m/sec given that the rate of flow remained 29,000 *l* per second.

(iii)

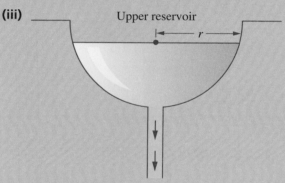

Upper reservoir

The cylindrical pipe drains water from an upper reservoir of hemispherical shape. It takes 4 hours at a constant flow rate of 29,000 *l* per second to empty the upper reservoir. Find, correct to the nearest integer, the depth in m of the water in the upper reservoir before the water began to flow.

Solution

(i)

key point

- Diameter 2·4 m $\Rightarrow$ Radius = 1·2 m
- 29,000 *l* = 29 m³, as 1,000 *l* = 1 m³
- Flow in pipe should be considered at 1-second intervals.

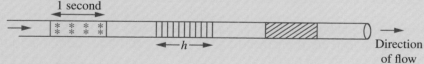

Then speed is *h* m/sec.
Rate of flow is 29 m³/sec.

Volume of water per second = Volume of cylinder = $\pi r^2 h$

$$29 = \pi(1·2)^2 h$$

$$6·4104 = h$$

(a) Speed = 6·4 m/sec

(b) Speed = $\dfrac{6·4 \times 60 \times 60}{1{,}000}$ = 23 km/h

Diameter halved (to 1·2 m) then radius = 0·6 m

Flow rate unchanged means 29 = $\pi(0·6)^2 h$

25·6 = $h \Rightarrow$ speed 25·6 m/sec

key point

Radius halved means r^2 decreases by a factor of $\left(\frac{1}{2}\right)^2 = \frac{1}{4}$.

(ii) Hence, to compensate for this decrease $\left(\text{of } \frac{1}{4}\right)$, the speed must increase by a factor of 4 if the rate of flow is unchanged.

(iii)

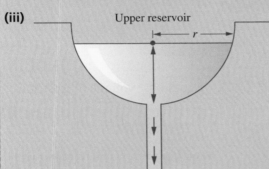

Upper reservoir

Flow rate of 29 m³/sec means

$29 \times 60 \times 60 \times 4 = 417{,}600$ m³ in 4 hours.

$\therefore$ Vol. hemisphere reservoir = $\dfrac{2}{3}\pi r^3$

$417{,}600 = \dfrac{2}{3}\pi r^3$

$58·420 = r$

Depth = 58 m to nearest integer

Example

A right circular cone S has dimensions given in cm, as in the diagram.
S is cut horizontally to its base and divided into two sections, P and Q, as shown.

(i) Write down the radius, R, of the cone S. Justify your answer for R.

(ii) Find the volume of S, correct to one decimal place, with $\pi = 3·14$.

(iii) Hence or otherwise, find the volume of the (frustum) section Q, correct to one decimal place, with $\pi = 3·14$.

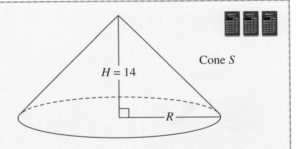

Cone S

$H = 14$

R

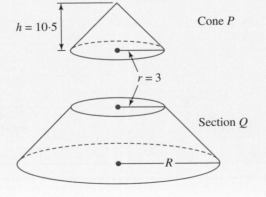

Cone P

$h = 10·5$

$r = 3$

Section Q

R

Solution

(i) We use similar triangles to calculate R.

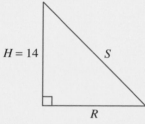 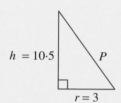

$$\frac{R}{r} = \frac{H}{h}$$

Hence, $\dfrac{R}{3} = \dfrac{14}{10\cdot5}$ becomes $10\cdot5R = 42.$ $\therefore R = 4\,\text{cm}$

(ii) Volume of $S = \dfrac{1}{3}\pi R^2 H = \dfrac{1}{3}\pi(4)^2(14) = 234\cdot6\,\text{cm}^3$

(iii) Volume Q = Volume S − Volume P | Or we could use volume of frustrum

$$= 234\cdot6 - \frac{1}{3}\pi r^2 h$$
$$= 234\cdot6 - \frac{1}{3}\pi(3)^2(10\cdot5)$$
$$= 234\cdot6 - 99$$
$$= 135\cdot6\,\text{cm}^3$$

$$= \frac{1}{3}\pi h[R^2 + Rr + r^2]$$

(from book of formulae and tables page 11)

$$= \frac{1}{3}\pi(14 - 10\cdot5)[16 + 12 + 9]$$
$$= \frac{1}{3}\pi(3\cdot5)(37) = 135\cdot6\,\text{cm}^3$$

exam focus

This type of procedural question on volumes can easily convert into an in-context exam question. For example:

Find in terms of r, R and π the volume of the lampshade in the diagram below.

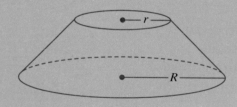

A regular tetrahedron has four faces, each of which is an equilateral triangle.

The tetrahedron is placed inside a cylindrical container with one face flat against the bottom, as shown in the diagram.

Given the length of one edge of the tetrahedron is $2x$, show that the volume of the smallest possible cylindrical container is $\dfrac{8\sqrt{6}\pi x^3}{9}$.

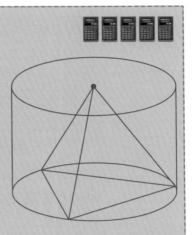

Solution

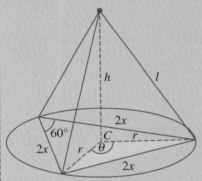

Note: Equilateral triangle has all angles 60°.

Since C is the centre of the circular base and a circle theorem states the angle of the centre of a circle is twice the angle at the circle standing on the same arc, then $\theta = 2(60°) = 120°$.

Hence:

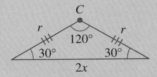

Using the sine rule, we write:

$$\frac{r}{\sin 30} = \frac{2x}{\sin 120} \Rightarrow \frac{r}{\frac{1}{2}} = \frac{2x}{\frac{\sqrt{3}}{2}}$$

$$\Rightarrow r = \frac{2x}{\sqrt{3}}$$

Lift out the highlighted triangle to find an expression for h.

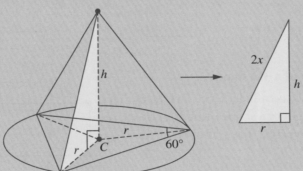

Use Pythagoras to write $(2x)^2 = (h)^2 + (r)^2$

$$4x^2 = h^2 + \left(\frac{2x}{\sqrt{3}}\right)^2$$

$$4x^2 = h^2 + \frac{4x^2}{3}$$

$$12x^2 = 3h^2 + 4x^2$$

$$8x^2 = 3h^2$$

$$\sqrt{\frac{8}{3}}x = h$$

Volume of cylinder $= \pi r^2 h = \pi\left(\frac{2x}{\sqrt{3}}\right)^2 \sqrt{\frac{8}{3}}x = \pi\frac{4x^2}{3}\sqrt{\frac{8}{3}}x$

$$= \pi\frac{4x^3}{3}\frac{2\sqrt{2}}{\sqrt{3}} = \frac{8\pi x^3 \sqrt{2}(\sqrt{3})}{3\sqrt{3}(\sqrt{3})} = \frac{8\sqrt{6}\pi x^3}{9}$$

Nets of 3D shapes

- When a 3D shape is opened out, the flat shape is called the **net**.

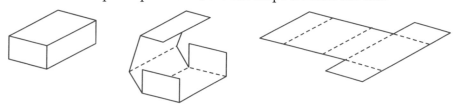

- This is how the net folds up to make a cuboid.

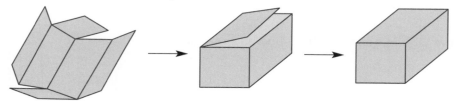

- **Naming parts of a 3D shape**
  Each flat surface is called a **face**. Two faces meet at an **edge**. Edges of a shape meet at a corner, or point, called a **vertex**. The plural of vertex is **vertices**.

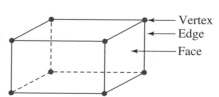

- This is how the net folds up to make a cylinder.

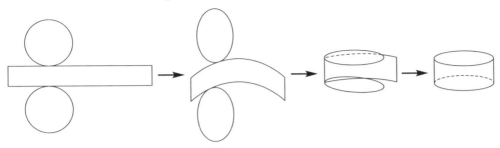

Note: There can be different nets for one solid cylinder.

(i) Express 165° in radians.

(ii) The diagram is a drawing of the net of a cone with vertex O.

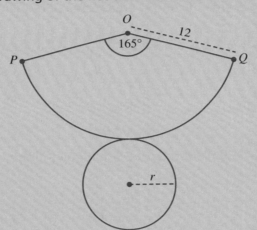

Show that the length of the minor arc PQ is 11π cm.

(iii) Hence or otherwise, find:

    (a) the total surface area of the cone

    (b) the volume of the cone.

    Give your answers correct to the nearest integer.

Solution

(i) $165° = \dfrac{165}{180}\pi = \dfrac{11}{12}\pi$ radians

(ii)

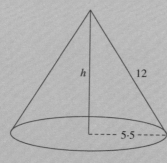

Length of minor arc PQ = (radius)(θ)

$$= (12)\left(\frac{11}{12}\pi\right)$$

$$= 11\pi \text{ cm}$$

(iii) (a) To find the total surface area, we require the radius, r, of the circle.

The circumference of the base of the cone = length of minor arc PQ.

$$2\pi r = 11\pi$$
$$r = 5 \cdot 5 \text{ cm}$$

Total surface area of cone = area sector OPQ + area circle

$$= \frac{1}{2}(\text{radius})^2\theta + \pi r^2$$

$$= \frac{1}{2}(12)^2\left(\frac{11}{12}\pi\right) + \pi(5 \cdot 5)^2$$

$$= 66\pi + 30 \cdot 25\pi$$

$$= 302 \text{ cm}^2$$

(b) To find the volume of the cone, we require h, the height of the cone.

$(12)^2 = h^2 + (5 \cdot 5)^2$ (by Pythagoras' theorem)

$$144 = h^2 + 30 \cdot 25$$
$$113 \cdot 75 = h^2$$
$$10 \cdot 66 = h$$

Volume of cone $= \frac{1}{3}\pi r^2 h = \frac{1}{3}\pi(5 \cdot 5)^2(10 \cdot 66) = 338 \text{ cm}^3$

The above procedural area and volume question can easily convert into an in-context exam question, as follows:

A company uses waterproof paper to make disposable conical (with a lid) drinking cups. To make each cup, a sector *POQ* and a circle, as shown in the diagram, are cut from a waterproof sheet of paper. The edges *PO* and *QO* are joined to form the cup, as shown.

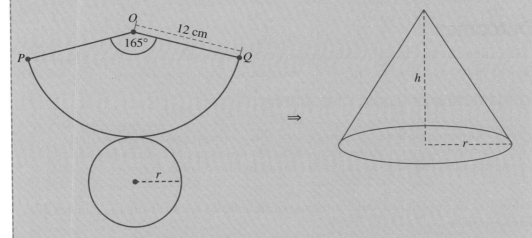

Find the radius, height and volume of such a conical cup.

In practice, would these dimensions be suitable for a drinking cup? Justify your answer.

Solution

We found radius = 5·5 cm
        Height = 10·66 cm
        Volume = 338 cm^3 = 0·338 l in the previous example

Overall, the radius and height are a bit bigger than a traditional cup, but acceptable.

Volume = 0·338 l = 338 ml is a suitable quantity for drinking.

Not sure about the lid. The pointed base of the cup is not very practical.

Conclusion: Dimensions are good but the design needs work!

8 Permutations and Combinations

aims

☐ To understand the two versions of the fundamental principle of counting

☐ To be able to calculate the number of arrangements (permutations) of objects

☐ To learn how to calculate the number of selections (combinations) of objects

☐ Solving equations involving $n!$ and $\binom{n}{r}$

Outcomes

The result of an operation is called an outcome. For example, if we throw a die, one possible outcome is 2. If we throw a die there are six possible outcomes: 1, 2, 3, 4, 5 or 6.

Fundamental principle of counting 1

> Suppose one operation has m possible outcomes and that a second operation has n outcomes. The number of possible outcomes when performing the first operation **followed by** the second operation is $m \times n$.

Performing one operation **and** another operation means we **multiply** the number of possible outcomes.

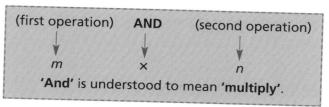

> (first operation)   **AND**   (second operation)
>
> $\quad\quad m \quad\quad\quad \times \quad\quad\quad n$
>
> 'And' is understood to mean 'multiply'.

Note: We assume that the outcome of one operation does not affect the number of possible outcomes of the other operation.

The fundamental principle of counting 1 can be extended to three or more operations.

Fundamental principle of counting 2

> Suppose one operation has m possible outcomes and that a second operation has n outcomes. Then the number of possible outcomes of the first operation **or** the second operation is given by $m + n$.

Performing one operation **or** another operation means we **add** the number of possible outcomes.

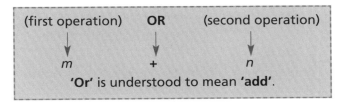

(first operation)   **OR**   (second operation)

$$m \qquad + \qquad n$$

'Or' is understood to mean **'add'**.

Note: We assume it is not possible for both operations to occur. In other words, there is no overlap of the two operations.

The fundamental principle of counting 2 can be extended to three or more operations, as long as none of the operations overlap.

key point

There are two key words when applying the fundamental principles of counting:

- **'And'** is understood to mean **'multiply'**. Thus, and means ×.
- **'Or'** is understood to mean **'add'**. Thus, or means +.

Permutations (arrangements)

A **permutation** is an arrangement of a number of objects in a definite order.

exam focus

Look out for the word **'arranged'** or **'arrangements'**. This indicates that the question is about **permutations**.

Example

A number-plate is to consist of three letters of the English alphabet followed by two digits. If no letter or digit can be repeated and 0 can never be used as the first digit, how many different plates can be manufactured?

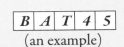

| B | A | T | 4 | 5 |

(an example)

Solution

Represent each choice with a box.

no 0

$\boxed{26} \times \boxed{25} \times \boxed{24} \times \boxed{9} \times \boxed{9} = 26 \times 25 \times 24 \times 9 \times 9 = 1{,}263{,}600$

exam focus

There are very few calculations involved with some of these questions, so it is very important that you show the method you used to solve the problem. **In general, the answer alone, with no workings, will not be awarded full marks.**

exam Q

At the Olympic Games, eight lanes are marked on the running track. Each runner is allocated to a different lane. Find the number of ways in which the runners in a heat can be allocated to these lanes when there are

(i) eight runners in the heat

(ii) five runners in the heat and any five lanes may be used.

Solution

(i) Number of ways lanes can be allocated

$= \boxed{8} \times \boxed{7} \times \boxed{6} \times \boxed{5} \times \boxed{4} \times \boxed{3} \times \boxed{2} \times \boxed{1} = 8! = 40{,}320$

(ii) Five runners. Any of the eight lanes can be used by the five runners. Number of ways lanes can be allocated

$= \boxed{8} \times \boxed{7} \times \boxed{6} \times \boxed{5} \times \boxed{4} = 6{,}720$ or $^{8}P_5 = 6{,}720$

key point

Factorial function (!)

A function on your calculator that instantly multiplies a number by all the numbers which come before it, down as far as 1.

$5 \times 4 \times 3 \times 2 \times 1 = 5! = 120$

$7 \times 6 \times 5 \times 4 \times 3 \times 2 \times 1 = 7! = 5{,}040$

Permutation function (^nP_r)

A function on your calculator that calculates the number of ways r objects can be arranged from n distinct objects.

Six objects permuted in three ways: $^6P_3 = 120$

Eight objects permuted in four ways: $^8P_4 = 1{,}680$

Restrictions

If there is a restriction on the arrangement (for example, the arrangement must begin with a D), put this restriction in first.

Example

The password for a mobile phone consists of five digits.

(i) How many passwords are possible?

(ii) How many of these passwords start with a 2 and finish with an odd digit?

Solution

(i) There are 10 digits: 0, 1, 2, 3, 4, 5, 6, 7, 8, 9.

Number of possible passwords $= \boxed{10} \times \boxed{10} \times \boxed{10} \times \boxed{10} \times \boxed{10} = 10^5 = 100{,}000$

(ii) The first position can be filled in only one way (2).

The fifth position can be filled in five ways (1 or 3 or 5 or 7 or 9).

The middle three positions can each be filled in 10 ways.

$$\overset{2}{\boxed{1}} \times \boxed{10} \times \boxed{10} \times \boxed{10} \times \overset{\text{odd}}{\boxed{5}} = 5{,}000$$

Thus, the number of possible passwords $= \boxed{1} \times \boxed{10} \times \boxed{10} \times \boxed{10} \times \boxed{5} = 5{,}000$

It is good practice to draw the boxes and **put the restriction above the box.** This makes it very clear to the examiner where your figures are coming from and the steps you took in reaching your solution.

Example

Two adults and four children stand in a row for a photograph.
How many different arrangements are possible if the four children are between the two adults?

Solution

The four children can stand in the middle in $\boxed{4} \times \boxed{3} \times \boxed{2} \times \boxed{1} = 4! = 24$ ways.

The two adults can stand on each side in $\boxed{2} \times \boxed{1} = 2! = 2$ ways.

Thus, the number of arrangements $= 2! \times 4! = 2 \times 24 = 48$.

Alternatively, the number of arrangements $= \boxed{2} \times \boxed{4} \times \boxed{3} \times \boxed{2} \times \boxed{1} \times \boxed{1} = 48$.

Example

P, Q, R, S, T, U and V are seven students. In how many ways can they stand in a row if:

  (i) there are no restrictions

 (ii) P and Q must sit beside each other

(iii) P and Q must **not** sit beside each other

(iv) T, U and V must sit beside each other

 (v) P or V must never sit at the end of each row.

Solution

 (i) **No restrictions**

    Number of arrangements $= \boxed{7} \times \boxed{6} \times \boxed{5} \times \boxed{4} \times \boxed{3} \times \boxed{2} \times \boxed{1} =$
                    $7! = 5,040$

(ii) **P and Q must sit beside each other**

    Consider P and Q as one person.

    $\boxed{P, Q}, R, S, T, U, V$

    The seven students (six objects) can be arranged in

    $\boxed{6} \times \boxed{5} \times \boxed{4} \times \boxed{3} \times \boxed{2} \times \boxed{1} = 6! = 720$ ways.

    But P and Q can be arranged in $\boxed{2} \times \boxed{1} = 2! = 2$ ways while seated together.

    Thus, the number of arrangements $= 2! \times 6! = 2 \times 720 = 1,440$.

(iii) P and Q must not sit beside each other

$$\begin{pmatrix}\text{Number of arrangements with} \\ P \text{ and } Q \text{ not together}\end{pmatrix} = \begin{pmatrix}\text{Total number} \\ \text{of arrangements}\end{pmatrix} - \begin{pmatrix}\text{Number of arrangements with} \\ P \text{ and } Q \text{ together}\end{pmatrix}$$

$$= 5{,}040 \qquad\qquad - 1{,}440$$
$$= 3{,}600$$

(iv) T, U and V must sit beside each other

Consider T, U and V as one person.

$P, Q, R, S, \boxed{T, U, V}$

The seven students (5 objects) can be arranged in

$\boxed{5} \times \boxed{4} \times \boxed{3} \times \boxed{2} \times \boxed{1} = 5! = 120$ ways.

But T, U and V can be arranged in $\boxed{3} \times \boxed{2} \times \boxed{1} = 3! = 6$ ways while seated together.

Thus, the number of arrangements $= 3! \times 5! = 6 \times 120 = 720$.

(v) P or V must never sit at the end of a row

The first position can be filled in five ways **and then** the last position in four ways.
Then the middle five positions can be filled in

$\boxed{5} \times \boxed{4} \times \boxed{3} \times \boxed{2} \times \boxed{1} = 5! = 120$ ways.

Number of arrangements $= \boxed{5} \times \boxed{5} \times \boxed{4} \times \boxed{3} \times \boxed{2} \times \boxed{1} \times \boxed{4} = 2{,}400$

This next example uses both fundamental principles of counting.

A bag contains nine discs, numbered from 1 to 9. A disc is drawn from the bag. If the number is prime, then a die is thrown. If the number is non-prime, then a coin is tossed. How many outcomes are possible?

Solution

Break the experiment into two different experiments and work out the number of outcomes separately. Then add the results.

Prime numbers: 2, 3, 5, 7
(4 outcomes)
Die: 1, 2, 3, 4, 5, 6 (6 outcomes)

Non-prime numbers: 1, 4, 6, 8, 9
(5 outcomes)
Coin: H, T (2 outcomes)

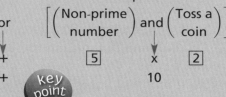

First experiment

$$\left[\begin{pmatrix}\text{Prime} \\ \text{number}\end{pmatrix} \text{ and } \begin{pmatrix}\text{Throw} \\ \text{a die}\end{pmatrix}\right] \quad \text{or}$$

$$= \quad \boxed{4} \quad \times \quad \boxed{6} \quad +$$
$$= \quad 24 \quad +$$
$$= \quad 34$$

Second experiment

$$\left[\begin{pmatrix}\text{Non-prime} \\ \text{number}\end{pmatrix} \text{ and } \begin{pmatrix}\text{Toss a} \\ \text{coin}\end{pmatrix}\right]$$

$$\boxed{5} \quad \times \quad \boxed{2}$$
$$10$$

key point

1 is not a prime number.

Combinations (selections)

A **combination** is a selection of a number of objects in any order.

Combinations function $(^nC_r) = \binom{n}{r}$

A function on your calculator that calculates the number of ways r objects can be selected from n distinct objects.

Four objects selected from seven objects: $^7C_4 = 35$

Three objects selected from nine objects: $^9C_3 = 84$

Example

A committee of five is to be selected from six students and three teachers.

  (i) How many different committees of five are possible?

 (ii) How many of these possible committees have three students and two teachers?

(iii) How many of these possible committees have more students than teachers?

Solution

6 students and 3 teachers = 9 people

  (i) **No restrictions**

Number of committees $= \binom{9}{5} = 126$

 (ii) **3 students and 2 teachers**

We have to choose three students from the six students **and** two teachers from the three teachers.

Number of committees $= \binom{6}{3} \times \binom{3}{2} = 20 \times 3 = 60$

(iii) **We need more students, S, than teachers, T**

Let $S =$ the number of students and $T =$ the number of teachers.

Possibilities are:

5 S and 0 T or   4 S and 1 T or   3 S and 2 T

Number of committees

$$= \binom{6}{5} \times \binom{3}{0} \quad + \quad \binom{6}{4} \times \binom{3}{1} \quad + \quad \binom{6}{3} \times \binom{3}{2}$$

$$= 6 \times 1 \quad + \quad 15 \times 3 \quad + \quad 20 \times 3$$

$$= 6 + 45 + 60 = 111$$

Example

A team of four is selected from a group of seven girls and five boys.

(i) How many different selections are possible?

(ii) How many of these selections include at least one girl?

Solution

7 girls + 5 boys = 12 people

(i) **No restrictions**

Number of selections $= \binom{12}{4} = 495$

(ii) In this case it is easier to calculate the number of selections with no girls and then subtract this from the total number of selections.
No girls means having exactly four boys on the team:

Number of selections $= \binom{5}{4} = 5$

$$\binom{\text{Number of selections}}{\text{with at least one girl}} = \binom{\text{Total number}}{\text{of selections}} - \binom{\text{Number of selections}}{\text{with no girls}}$$

$$= 495 - 5 = 490$$

'At least one girl' means one girl or more. In this example: 1 girl and 3 boys or 2 girls and 2 boys or 3 girls and 1 boy or 4 girls and 0 boys.

Ten distinct points are taken on the circumference of a circle (as shown).

(i) (a) Calculate the number of different chords that can be formed using these points as end points.

(b) How many different triangles can be formed using these points as vertices?

(ii) (a) Calculate the number of different quadrilaterals that can be formed using these points as vertices.

(b) Two of the 10 points are labelled x and y, respectively. How many of the above quadrilaterals have x and y as vertices?

(c) How many of the quadrilaterals do not have x and y as vertices?

Solution

(i) (a) **Number of chords**

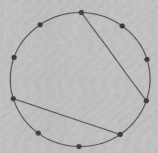

We have 10 points.
Each chord uses two points.

∴ Number of chords
$$= \binom{10}{2} = 45$$

(b) **Number of triangles**

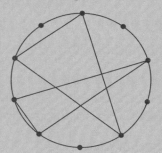

We have 10 points.
Each triangle uses three points.

∴ Number of triangles
$$= \binom{10}{3} = 120$$

(ii) (a) **Number of quadrilaterals**

We have 10 points.

Each quadrilateral uses four points.

∴ Number of quadrilaterals
$$= \binom{10}{4} = 210$$

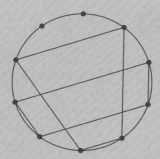

(b) Number of quadrilaterals with *x* and *y* as vertices.

We have 10 points.

Each quadrilateral uses four points.

But two of these, *x* and *y*, are fixed.

Thus, we have eight points from which we can choose two.

∴ Number of quadrilaterals with *x* and *y* as

$$\text{vertices} = \binom{8}{2} = 28$$

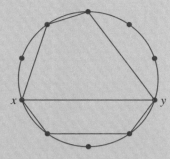

(c) $\left(\begin{array}{c}\text{Number of quadrilaterals}\\ \text{with } [xy] \text{ as vertices}\end{array}\right) = \left(\begin{array}{c}\text{Total number of}\\ \text{quadrilaterals}\end{array}\right) - \left(\begin{array}{c}\text{Number of quadrilaterals}\\ \text{with } [xy] \text{ as vertices}\end{array}\right)$

$$= 210 - 28 = 182$$

Equations involving *n*! and $\binom{n}{r}$

Sometimes we have to solve equations involving $\binom{n}{r}$.

In these questions, we make use of the following:

$$\binom{n}{1} = \frac{n}{1} = n \qquad \binom{n}{2} = \frac{n(n-1)}{(2)(1)} = \frac{n^2-n}{2} \qquad \binom{n}{3} = \frac{n(n-1)(n-2)}{(3)(2)(1)}$$

$$\frac{(n+1)!}{n!} = \frac{(n+1)n!}{n!} = n+1$$

key point

- $\binom{n}{o} = \binom{n}{n} = 1$

- *n* and *r* must be positive whole numbers, where *r* can be zero, but *n* can't.

- $n \geq r$

Example

Solve: **(i)** $\binom{n}{2} = 36$ **(ii)** $\binom{n+1}{2} = 10\binom{n}{1}$, where $n \in \mathbb{N}$

Solution

(i)
$$\binom{n}{2} = 36$$

$$\frac{n(n-1)}{2} = 36$$

$$n(n-1) = 72$$

$$n^2 - n = 72$$

$$n^2 - n - 72 = 0$$

$$(n+8)(n-9) = 0$$

$$n = -8 \quad \text{or} \quad n = 9$$

Reject $n = -8$, as $-8 \notin \mathbb{N}$.

$$\therefore n = 9$$

Check: $\binom{9}{2} = 36$ (correct)

(ii)
$$\binom{n+1}{2} = 10\binom{n}{1}$$

$$\frac{n(n+1)}{2} = 10(n)$$

$$n(n+1) = 20(n)$$

$$n^2 + n = 20n$$

$$n^2 - 19n = 0$$

$$n(n-19) = 0$$

$$n = 0 \quad \text{or} \quad n = 19$$

Reject $n = 0$, as $0 \notin \mathbb{N}$.

$$\therefore n = 19$$

Check: $\binom{20}{2} = 190$

$$10\binom{19}{1} = 190 \quad \text{(correct)}$$

Example

Solve $\dfrac{n!}{(n-2)!} = 90$, when $n \in \mathbb{N}$ and $n \geq 2$.

Solution

$$\frac{n!}{(n-2)!} = 90$$

$$\frac{n(n-1)(n-2)!}{(n-2)!} = 90$$

$$\left(\frac{n!}{(n-2)!} = \frac{n(n-1)(n-2)!}{(n-2)!}\right)$$

$$n(n-1) = 90$$

(divide top and bottom by $(n-2)!$)

$$n^2 - n = 90$$

$$n^2 - n - 90 = 0$$

$$(n+9)(n-10) = 0$$

$$n = -9 \quad \text{or} \quad n = 10$$

Reject $n = -9$, as $-9 \notin \mathbb{N}$.

$$\therefore n = 10$$

Check: $\dfrac{10!}{8!} = \dfrac{10 \times 9 \times 8!}{8!} = 10 \times 9 = 90$ (correct)

9 Probability

☐ To learn the language of probability
☐ To understand the rules of probability and how to apply these rules
☐ To learn the difference between mutually exclusive and independent events
☐ How to deal with conditional probability
☐ To become proficient at dealing with the examination aspect of counting and probability

Probability involves the study of the laws of chance. It is a measure of the chance, or likelihood, of something happening.

If you carry out an operation, or experiment, using coins, dice, spinners or cards, then each toss, throw, spin or draw is called a **trial**.

The possible things that can happen from a trial are called **outcomes**. The outcomes of interest are called an **event**. In other words, an event is the set of successful outcomes.

If E is an event, then $P(E)$ stands for the probability that the event occurs. $P(E)$ is read as 'the probability of E'.

The probability of an event is a number between 0 and 1, including 0 and 1.

$$0 \leq P(E) \leq 1$$

The value of $P(E)$ can be given as a fraction, decimal or percentage.

Note: $P(E) = 0$ means that an event is **impossible**.
$P(E) = 1$ means that an event is **certain**.

Formulae:

The measure of the probability of an event, E, is given by:

$$P(E) = \frac{\text{Number of successful outcomes}}{\text{Number of possible outcomes}}$$

$P(E) + P(\text{not } E) = 1$

or

$P(\text{not } E) = 1 - P(E)$

key point

$P(\text{not } E)$ is sometimes written $P(\bar{E})$ or $P(E')$.

The probability that two events, A or B, can happen is given by:

$$P(A \text{ or } B) = P(A) + P(B) - P(A \text{ and } B)$$

(removes double counting)

Mutually exclusive events

$P(A \cap B) = 0$ (no double counting)

Conditional probability

$$P(A|B) = \frac{P(A \cap B)}{P(B)}$$

Independent events

1. $P(A|B) = P(A)$ **2.** $P(B|A) = P(B)$ **3.** $P(A \cap B) = P(A) \times P(B)$

Any one of 1, 2 or 3 is sufficient to prove independence.

General multiplication rule: $P(A \text{ and } B) = P(A) \times P(B|A)$

Note: If A and B are independent events, then $P(A \text{ and } B) = P(A) \times P(B)$.

Do not confuse mutually exclusive events and independent events.

Mutually exclusive events are events that cannot happen together.
For mutually exclusive events A and B: **$P(A \text{ and } B) = 0$.**   (no double counting)

Independent events are events that can happen at the same time or can happen one after the other. For independent events A and B:

$$P(A \text{ and } B) = P(A) \times P(B) \text{ or } P(A|B) = P(A) \text{ or } P(B|A) = P(B)$$

Independent events cannot be mutually exclusive and mutually exclusive events cannot be independent.

Example

A and B are two events such that $P(A) = 0.6$ and $P(B) = 0.2$.
What is $P(A \cup B)$ if:

  (i) A and B are mutually exclusive
 (ii) A and B are independent.

Solution

(i) A and B are mutually exclusive.

$$\therefore P(A \cap B) = 0$$

$$\begin{aligned} P(A \cup B) &= P(A) + P(B) \\ &\quad - P(A \cap B) \\ &= 0.6 + 0.2 - 0 \\ &= 0.8 \end{aligned}$$

(ii) A and B are independent.

$$\begin{aligned} \therefore P(A \cap B) &= P(A) \times P(B) \\ &= 0.6 \times 0.2 = 0.12 \end{aligned}$$

$$\begin{aligned} P(A \cup B) &= P(A) + P(B) \\ &\quad - P(A \cap B) \\ &= 0.6 + 0.2 - 0.12 \\ &= 0.68 \end{aligned}$$

Give an example of:

 (i) two mutually exclusive events
(ii) two non-mutually exclusive events.

Solution

 (i) If you throw a die once, it is impossible to obtain an odd number and an even number.

P(odd number and a even number on one throw of a normal die) = 0

(no double counting)

∴ Obtaining an odd number and an even on one throw of a normal die are mutually exclusive events.

(ii) If you draw one card from a normal 52-card deck of cards, it is possible to obtain an ace and a diamond.

P(drawing an ace and a diamond) $\neq 0$. (It is actually equal to $\frac{1}{52}$.)

∴ Obtaining an ace and a diamond from a normal 52-card deck of cards are non-mutually exclusive events.

Example

A and B are independent events such that $P(A) = 0.2$ and $P(A \cup B) = 0.55$.
Find $P(B)$.

Solution

A and B are independent events. Therefore, $P(A \cap B) = P(A) \times P(B)$.

$$P(A \cup B) = P(A) + P(B) - P(A \cap B)$$
$$P(A \cup B) = P(A) + P(B) - P(A) \times P(B) \qquad (A \text{ and } B \text{ are independent})$$
$$0.55 = 0.2 + P(B) - 0.2P(B)$$
$$0.55 = 0.2 + 0.8P(B) \qquad (P(B) - 0.2P(B) = 0.8P(B))$$
$$0.35 = 0.8P(B)$$
$$P(B) = \frac{0.35}{0.8} = \frac{35}{80} = \frac{7}{16} \quad \text{or} \quad 0.4375$$

Two events, A and B, are such that $P(A) = 0.2$, $P(A \cap B) = 0.15$ and
$P(A' \cap B) = 0.6$.

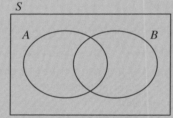

(i) Complete this Venn diagram.

(ii) Find the probability that neither
A nor B happens.

(iii) Find the conditional probability $P(A|B)$.

(iv) State whether A and B are independent
events and justify your answer.

Solution

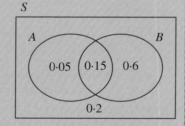

(i) $A' \cap B$ is the region B only or $B\backslash A$.
$$P(A' \cap B) = P(B\backslash A) = P(B \text{ only}) = 0.6$$
$$P(A \cap B) = 0.15$$
$$P(A\backslash B) = P(A) - P(A \cap B) = 0.2 - 0.15 = 0.05$$

(ii) $P[S\backslash(A \cup B)] = P(\text{neither } A \text{ nor } B)$
$$= 1 - 0.05 - 0.15 - 0.6 = 0.2$$

(iii) $P(A|B) = \dfrac{P(A \cap B)}{P(B)} = \dfrac{0.15}{0.75} = 0.2 \qquad [P(B) = 0.15 + 0.6 = 0.75]$

(iv) $P(A|B) = 0.2$ $\qquad$ $P(A) = 0.2$

$\quad$ $P(A|B) = P(A)$ $\qquad\qquad$ $\therefore$ A and B are independent events.

$$\text{or}$$

$\quad$ $P(B|A) = 0.15 + 0.6 = 0.75$ $\qquad$ $P(B) = 0.75$

$\quad$ $P(B|A) = P(B)$ $\qquad\qquad\qquad$ $\therefore$ A and B are independent events.

$$\text{or}$$

$\quad$ $P(A) \times P(B) = 0.2 \times 0.75 = 0.15$ $\qquad$ $P(A \cap B) = 0.15$

$\quad$ $P(A) \times P(B) = P(A \cap B)$ $\qquad\qquad$ $\therefore$ A and B are independent events.

Four students work separately on a mathematical problem. The probability that the four students have of solving the problem is as follows: $\dfrac{7}{8}, \dfrac{3}{4}, \dfrac{1}{3}$ and $\dfrac{2}{7}$.

Show the probability that the problem will be solved by at least one of the four students is $\dfrac{331}{336}$.

Solution

Let the students be A, B, C and D.

Let $P(S)$ = probability of solving the problem and $P(F)$ = probability of failing to solve the problem.

	A	B	C	D
P(S)	$\dfrac{7}{8}$	$\dfrac{3}{4}$	$\dfrac{1}{3}$	$\dfrac{2}{7}$
P(F)	$\dfrac{1}{8}$	$\dfrac{1}{4}$	$\dfrac{2}{3}$	$\dfrac{5}{7}$

P(all four fail to solve the problem)

$= P(A_F \text{ and } B_F \text{ and } C_F \text{ and } D_F)$

$= P(A_F) \times P(B_F) \times P(C_F) \times P(D_F)$

$= \dfrac{1}{8} \times \dfrac{1}{4} \times \dfrac{2}{3} \times \dfrac{5}{7} = \dfrac{5}{336}$

P(at least one will solve the problem) $= 1 - P$(all four fail to solve the problem)

$$= 1 - \dfrac{5}{336} = \dfrac{331}{336}$$

Note: $P(A_F)$ = probability that A fails to solve the problem and so on.

The phrase 'at least one' occurs in many probability problems. 'At least one' means 'one or more'. In the above problem it means one or two or three or four students solve the problem.

TREE DIAGRAMS

- If a question says 'using a tree diagram', then you **must** use a tree diagram.
- If a question says 'using a tree diagram or otherwise', then other methods are accepted.
- Tree diagrams display all possible mutually exclusive events.
- The sum of the probabilities on **any set** of branches always adds up to 1.
- Multiply the probabilities along the branches to get the end result.
- If more than one set of end results are required, simply add the end results together.
- It is good practice to check that the sum of all the probabilities is 1.

If Mr Smith has a good week at work (which happens 70% of the time), there's a 0·8 probability that he will take the family out to a restaurant on Friday evening, otherwise they'll eat at home. If he's had a bad week there is only a 0·3 probability of eating in a restaurant on Friday evening.

(i) By making a tree diagram or otherwise, calculate:

(a) the probability that the family eat at a restaurant on a Friday

(b) the probability that Mr Smith had a good week at work, given that they ate at a restaurant on a certain Friday.

(ii) A restaurant meal will cost the family €100, while a meal at home will only cost €20. Find the expected cost of their Friday evening meal.

Solution

Let G = P(good day), B = P(bad day), M = P(meal out) and H = P(meal at home).

(i) (a)

G and M = 0·7 × 0·8 = 0·56

G and H = 0·7 × 0·2 = 0·14

B and M = 0·3 × 0·3 = 0·09

B and H = 0·3 × 0·7 = 0·21

(Check: Sum of the probabilities = 0·56 + 0·14 + 0·09 + 0·21 = 1)

P(meal out)

$$= P(M) = P(G \text{ and } M) + P(B \text{ and } M) = 0.56 + 0.09 = 0.65 \text{ or } \frac{13}{20}$$

(b) P(Mr Smith had a good week at work, given that the family ate out)

$$= P(G|M) = \frac{P(G \text{ and } M)}{P(M)} = \frac{0\cdot56}{0\cdot65} = \frac{56}{65}$$

(ii)

	Meal out (M)	Meal home (H)
x	€100	€20
$P(x)$	0·65	0·35

Expected cost
$= E(x)$
$= \Sigma x P(x)$
$= 100(0\cdot65) + 20(0\cdot35)$
$= 65 + 7 = 72$

∴ The expected cost = €72.

There are 16 discs in a board game: five blue, three green, six red and two yellow. Four discs are chosen at random. What is the probability that:

(i) the four discs are blue

(ii) the four discs are the same colour

(iii) all four discs are different colours

(iv) two of the discs are blue and two are not blue?

Solution

Method 1: Picking one at a time

Let B_1 represent that a blue disc is chosen first, R_2 represent that a red disc is chosen second, and so on.

(i) P(all four discs are blue)

$$= P(B_1 \text{ and } B_2 \text{ and } B_3 \text{ and } B_4) = P(B_1) \times P(B_2) \times P(B_3) \times P(B_4)$$

$$= \frac{5}{16} \times \frac{4}{15} \times \frac{3}{14} \times \frac{2}{13} = \frac{1}{364}$$

(ii) P(all four discs are the same colour)

$$= P(4B) + P(4R)$$

$$= P(B_1 \text{ and } B_2 \text{ and } B_3 \text{ and } B_4) + P(R_1 \text{ and } R_2 \text{ and } R_3 \text{ and } R_4)$$

$$= P(B_1) \times P(B_2) \times P(B_3) \times P(B_4) + P(R_1) \times P(R_2) \times P(R_3) \times P(R_4)$$

$$= \frac{5}{16} \times \frac{4}{15} \times \frac{3}{14} \times \frac{2}{13} + \frac{6}{16} \times \frac{5}{16} \times \frac{4}{14} \times \frac{3}{13} = \frac{1}{364} + \frac{3}{364} = \frac{4}{364} = \frac{1}{91}$$

(iii) The four colours blue, green, red and yellow can occur in 4! ways (or 24 ways).

P(all four discs are different colours)

$$= P(B_1 \text{ and } G_2 \text{ and } R_3 \text{ and } Y_4) \times 4! \qquad \text{(or any other arrangement)}$$

$$= P(B_1) \times P(G_2) \times P(R_3) \times P(Y_4) \times 4!$$

$$= \frac{5}{16} \times \frac{3}{15} \times \frac{6}{14} \times \frac{2}{13} \times 24 = \frac{4,320}{43,680} = \frac{9}{91}$$

(iv) The four colours, blue, blue, not B, not B, can occur in $\frac{4!}{2!\,2!}$ ways (or six ways).

P(two of the discs are blue and two are not blue)

$= P(B_1 \text{ and } B_2 \text{ and } B'_3 \text{ and } B'_4)$ (B' means not blue)

$= P(B_1) \times P(B_2) \times P(B'_3) \times P(B'_4) \times 6$

$= \dfrac{5}{16} \times \dfrac{4}{15} \times \dfrac{11}{14} \times \dfrac{10}{13} \times 6 = \dfrac{13{,}200}{43{,}680} = \dfrac{55}{182}$

Method 2: Using combinations

(i) P(all four discs are blue) $= \dfrac{\binom{5}{4}}{\binom{16}{4}} = \dfrac{5}{1{,}820} = \dfrac{1}{364}$

(ii) P(all four discs are the same colour)

$= P(4 \text{ blue}) + P(4 \text{ red}) = \dfrac{\binom{5}{4}}{\binom{16}{4}} + \dfrac{\binom{6}{4}}{\binom{16}{4}} = \dfrac{5}{1{,}820} + \dfrac{15}{1{,}820} = \dfrac{20}{1{,}820} = \dfrac{1}{91}$

(iii) P(all four discs are the same colour)

$= \dfrac{\binom{5}{1} \times \binom{3}{1} \times \binom{6}{1} \times \binom{2}{1}}{\binom{16}{4}} = \dfrac{5 \times 3 \times 6 \times 2}{1{,}820} = \dfrac{180}{1{,}820} = \dfrac{9}{91}$

(iv) P(two of the discs are blue and two are not blue)

$= \dfrac{\binom{5}{2} \times \binom{11}{2}}{\binom{16}{4}} = \dfrac{10 \times 55}{1{,}820} = \dfrac{550}{1{,}820} = \dfrac{55}{182}$

There are 16 girls and eight boys in a class. Half of these 24 students study French. The probability that a randomly selected girl studies French is 1·5 times the probability that a randomly selected boy studies French. How many of the boys in the class study French?

Solution

There are 24 pupils in this class: 16 girls and eight boys. 12 study French.

Let x = the number of boys who study French
and let y = the number of girls who study French.

$\therefore x + y = 12$ or $y = 12 - x$

$$P(\text{girl studies French}) = \frac{\text{Number of girls who study French}}{\text{Number of girls}} = \frac{y}{16} = \frac{12 - x}{16}$$

$$P(\text{boy studies French}) = \frac{\text{Number of boys who study French}}{\text{Number of boys}} = \frac{x}{8}$$

Given: $P(\text{girl studies French}) = 1 \cdot 5 \, P(\text{boy studies French})$

$$\therefore \qquad \frac{y}{16} = 1 \cdot 5 \left(\frac{x}{8}\right)$$

$$\therefore \qquad \frac{12 - x}{16} = 1 \cdot 5 \left(\frac{x}{8}\right) \qquad (y = 12 - x)$$

$$\frac{16(12 - x)}{16} = 16(1 \cdot 5)\left(\frac{x}{8}\right) \qquad \text{(multiply both sides by 16)}$$

$$12 - x = 3x$$

$$4x = 12$$

$$x = 3$$

Thus, three boys in this class study French.

In a recent exam this question was so badly answered that it was worth only 5 marks.

A bag contains discs of three different colours. There are five red discs, one white disc and x black discs. Three discs are picked together at random.

(i) Write down an expression in x for the probability that the three discs are all different colours.

(ii) If the probability that the three discs are all different colours is equal to the probability that they are all black, find x.

Solution

$5R, 1W, xB$ Total $(x + 6)$

(i) $P(\text{discs are all different colours})$

$$= P(R) \times P(W) \times P(B)$$

$$= \frac{5}{x + 6} \times \frac{1}{x + 5} \times \frac{x}{x + 4} = \frac{5x}{(x + 6)(x + 5)(x + 4)}$$

But this can occur $3!$ or six different ways.

$\therefore \quad P(\text{discs are all different colours})$

$$= 6\left(\frac{5x}{(x + 6)(x + 5)(x + 4)}\right) = \frac{30x}{(x + 6)(x + 5)(x + 4)}$$

(ii) $P(\text{all three are black}) = P(B_1) \times P(B_2) \times P(B_3)$

$$= \frac{x}{x + 6} \times \frac{x - 1}{x + 5} \times \frac{x - 2}{x + 4} = \frac{x(x - 1)(x - 2)}{(x + 6)(x + 5)(x + 4)}$$

Given:

$P(\text{discs are all different colours}) = P(\text{all three are black})$

$$\frac{30x}{(x + 6)(x + 5)(x + 4)} = \frac{x(x - 1)(x - 2)}{(x + 6)(x + 5)(x + 4)}$$

$$30 = (x - 1)(x - 2)$$

$$x^2 - 3x - 28 = 0$$

$$(x + 4)(x - 7) = 0$$

$$x = -4 \quad \text{or} \quad x = 7$$

$$\text{Reject } x = -4$$

$$\therefore x = 7$$

Estimating probabilities from experiments

Often a probability can only be found by carrying out a series of experiments and recording the results. For example, if you drop a drawing pin and you want to find the probability that it lands point up, there is no obvious method except by dropping a lot of drawing pins and recording the results. The probability of the event can then be **estimated** from these results. A probability found in this way is known as **experimental probability** or **relative frequency** of an event. Each separate experiment carried out is called a **trial**. To find the relative frequency, the experiment has to be repeated a number of times. It is important to remember that if an experiment is repeated, there will be different outcomes and that increasing the number of times an experiment is repeated generally leads to better estimates of probability.

Estimating probabilities using relative frequency

The relative frequency of an event in an experiment is given by:

$P(E) = \text{Relative frequency of an event} = \dfrac{\text{Number of successful trials}}{\text{Number of trials}}$

Relative frequency can be used to estimate how many times you would **expect** a particular outcome to happen in an experiment.

The expected number of outcomes (or expected value) is calculated as follows.

> Expected number of outcomes = (relative frequency) × (number of trials)
>
> or
>
> Expected number of outcomes = P(event) × (number of trials)

Note: To estimate the probability of some events, it is necessary to carry out a survey or look at historical data (past data).

Three casino managers, A, B and C, meet to consider a new type of four-sided die with numbers 1, 2, 3 and 4. To use the die in their casino it must be fair. At the meeting they each throw the die a number of times. The results are recorded in the table below.

Casino	Number of throws	1	2	3	4
A	30	5	8	10	7
B	45	8	13	15	9
C	61	9	14	22	16

(i) Which manager's results are more likely to give the best estimate of the probability of obtaining each number occuring? Justify your answer.

(ii) Calculate the relative frequency of manager A obtaining a score of 3.

(iii) If the die is fair, write down the probability of obtaining each number.

(iv) Calculate the relative frequency for each number on this die for all three managers' results.

(v) In your opinion, should the casinos use this die? Justify your answer.

Solution

(i) Manager C. He has thrown the die more times. The more times you throw the die, the more accurate the estimate of the probability of each number occuring.

(ii) $\dfrac{\text{Relative frequency of}}{\text{Manager A obtaining a 3}} = \dfrac{\text{Number of successful trials}}{\text{Number of trials}} = \dfrac{10}{30} = \dfrac{1}{3}$

(iii) If the die was fair, the probability of obtaining each number would be $\frac{1}{4}$.

(iv)

Number	1	2	3	4
Frequency	22	35	47	32
Relative frequency	$\dfrac{22}{136}$	$\dfrac{35}{136}$	$\dfrac{47}{136}$	$\dfrac{32}{136}$

(v) If the die was fair, each number should occur about the same number of times. In other words, each number should occur about $\dfrac{136}{4} = 34$ times.

Also, the relative frequency of each number should be close to $\dfrac{34}{136}$. The result of this experiment is that the relative frequency of 2 and 4 is close to $\dfrac{34}{136}$.

However, the relative frequency of 3, $\dfrac{47}{136}$, is well above $\dfrac{34}{136}$ and the relative frequency of 1, $\dfrac{22}{136}$, is well below $\dfrac{34}{136}$.

The result of this experiment appears to show that the die is biased in favour of 3 and biased against 1. Thus, I would recommend that the casinos do **not** use this die. However, the die was only thrown 136 times. The accuracy of the estimate of the probability of each number occuring could be improved if the die was thrown, and the results recorded, many more times. I would suggest about 1,000 times to improve the accuracy of the results.

Normal distribution and probability

One reason the normal distribution is so important is that the measurement of many natural phenomena are normally distributed (or nearly so), such as heights, weights, IQ scores and examination results. (See Chapter on Statistics IV for more on the normal distribution.)

- The z transformation is given by $z = \dfrac{x - \mu}{\sigma}$.
- The area under the curve of **any** normal curve is **always** equal to 1.

Finding areas under the normal curves

The mathematical tables give us the area to the left of a specified value of z. The table can be used to obtain a required area. The three graphs below summarise how to use the tables from the booklet of formulae and tables. **A copy of this table can also be found at the end of this book.**

Working with the normal curve is a vital skill in both probability and statistics.

1.	2.	3.
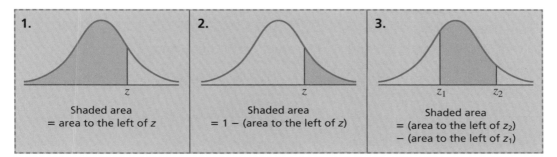		
z	z	$z_1 \quad z_2$
Shaded area = area to the left of z	Shaded area = 1 − (area to the left of z)	Shaded area = (area to the left of z_2) − (area to the left of z_1)

Note: Alternative to graph 3: Find the area to the left of z_1 and the area to the right of z_2 and subtract both from 1.

Some questions require that the table for normal distribution probabilities is read in reverse.

Example

A random variable, x, follows a normal distribution with mean 20 and standard deviation 5. Find $P(16 \le x \le 26)$.

Solution

Given: $\mu = 20$, $\sigma = 5$, $x_1 = 16$ and $x_2 = 26$. Find $P(16 \le x \le 26)$.
We first convert the x-values into z-values using $z = \frac{x - \mu}{\sigma}$.

$$z_1 = \frac{x_1 - \mu}{\sigma} \qquad\qquad z_2 = \frac{x_2 - \mu}{\sigma}$$

$$= \frac{16 - 20}{5} = \frac{-4}{5} = -0.8 \qquad = \frac{26 - 20}{5} = \frac{6}{5} = 1.2$$

Area under the curve between
$z_1 = -0.8$ and $z_2 = 1.2$
$\quad = 1 - 0.1151 - 0.2119$
$\quad = 0.673$
$P(16 \le x \le 26) = 0.673$

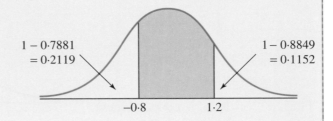

$1 - 0.7881$
$= 0.2119$

$1 - 0.8849$
$= 0.1152$

$-0.8 \qquad\qquad 1.2$

exam Q

In a normal distribution, a raw score of 56 corresponds to a z-score of 1 and a raw score of 60 corresponds to a z-score of 2. Find
(i) the standard deviation and **(ii)** the mean of this distribution.

Solution
Given: $x_1 = 56$ and $z_1 = 1$ and $x_2 = 60$ and $z_2 = 2$. Find σ and μ.

$$\frac{x_1 - \mu}{\sigma} = z_1$$

$$\frac{56 - \mu}{\sigma} = 1$$

$$56 - \mu = \sigma$$

$$\mu + \sigma = 56 \quad ①$$

$$\frac{x_2 - \mu}{\sigma} = z_2$$

$$\frac{60 - \mu}{\sigma} = 2$$

$$60 - \mu = 2\sigma$$

$$\mu + 2\sigma = 60 \quad ②$$

Solving the simultaneous equations ① and ② gives $\sigma = 4$ and $\mu = 52$.

∴ **(i)** Standard deviation = 4 and **(ii)** mean = 52.

exam focus

Notice the ability to solve linear simultaneous equations from algebra is essential to finish the above question on the normal curve.

Example

The heights of students in a certain class are normally distributed with a mean of 165 cm and a standard deviation of 10 cm. If 90% of the students in this class have a height of less than or equal to x cm, find the value of x.

Solution

$$\frac{x - \mu}{\sigma} = z$$

Reading the tables in reverse, the closest to 0·9 is 0·8997. This gives a z-value of 1·28.

Given: $\mu = 165, \sigma = 10$ and $z = 1·28$. Find x.

$$\frac{x - 165}{10} = 1·28$$

$$x - 165 = 12·8$$

$$x = 177·8$$

Thus, we conclude that 90% of these students have a height of 177·8 cm or less.

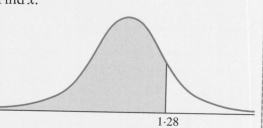

1·28

In the next example, the x values are not obvious.

A company produces calculator batteries. The diameter of the batteries is supposed to be 20 mm. The tolerance is 0·25 mm. Any batteries outside this tolerance are rejected. You may assume that this is the only reason for rejecting the batteries.

(i) The company has a machine that produces batteries with diameters that are normally distributed with a mean of 20 mm and a standard deviation of 0·1 mm. Out of every 10,000 batteries produced by this machine, how many, on average, are rejected?

(ii) A setting on the machine slips, so that the mean diameter of the batteries increases to 20·05 mm, while the standard deviation remains unchanged. Find the percentage increase in the rejection rate for batteries from this machine.

Solution

(i) $x_1 = 20 -$ tolerance $= 20 - 0·25 = 19·75$

$x_2 = 20 +$ tolerance $= 20 + 0·25 = 20·25$

Given: $\mu = 20$, $\sigma = 0·1$, $x_1 = 19·75$ and $x_2 = 20·25$.
Find $P(x \le 19·75) + P(x \ge 20·25)$.

We first convert the x-values into z-values using $z = \dfrac{x - \mu}{\sigma}$.

$z_1 = \dfrac{x_1 - \mu}{\sigma}$

$= \dfrac{19·75 - 20}{0·1} = \dfrac{-0·25}{0·1} = -2·5$

$z_2 = \dfrac{x_2 - \mu}{\sigma}$

$= \dfrac{20·25 - 20}{0·1} = \dfrac{0·25}{0·1} = 2·5$

$P(z \le -2·5) + P(z \ge 2·5)$

$= 0·0062 + 0·0062$

$= 0·0124$

0·0062   0·0062

$-2·5$ $2·5$

$\therefore$ $P(x \le 19·75) + P(x \ge 20·25) = P(z \le -2·5) + P(z \ge 2·5) = 0·0124$

Number of rejected batteries $= np = 10,000(0·0124) = 124$

(ii) New mean $= \mu = 20·05$

$z_1 = \dfrac{x_1 - \mu}{\sigma}$

$= \dfrac{19·75 - 20·05}{0·1} = \dfrac{-0·3}{0·1} = -3$

$z_2 = \dfrac{x_2 - \mu}{\sigma}$

$= \dfrac{20·25 - 20·05}{0·1} = \dfrac{0·2}{0·1} = 2$

$P(z \leq -3) + P(z \geq 2)$

$= 0.0013 + 0.0228$

$= 0.0241$

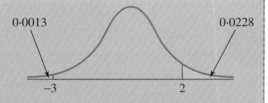

0.0013

0.0228

-3

2

$P(x \leq 19.75) + P(x \geq 20.25) = P(z \leq -3) + P(z \geq 2) = 0.0241$

Increase $= 0.0241 - 0.0124 = 0.0117$

Percentage increase $= \left(\dfrac{0.0117}{0.0124}\right) \times 100 = 94.35\%$

It is vital to know that in the examination:

(i) was awarded 20 marks while

(ii) was awarded 5 marks.

Remember, this type of examiner's marking adjustment is by no means an isolated incident. Keep moving through the questions to avoid 'time trouble'.

Binomial distribution (Bernoulli trials)

An experiment that satisfies the following four conditions is called a binomial distribution or a Bernoulli trial.

1. A fixed number, n, of repeated trials
2. Only two possible outcomes in each trial: success or failure
3. The trials are independent
4. The probability of a success in each trial is constant

In this situation, we let:

$p = P(\text{success})$ and $q = P(\text{failure})$, where $(p + q) = 1$.

$$P(r \text{ successes}) = \binom{n}{r} p^r q^{n-r}$$

Method

1. Write down n, the number of trials.
2. Calculate p and q ($q = 1 - p$).
3. Let r = number of successes required.
4. Use the formula above.

Examples of Bernoulli trials are:

1. Tossing coins   **2.** Shots in a competition   **3.** A search for defective products

Example

A factory manufactures light bulbs. Over a long period of time it was found that 5% of the bulbs were defective. An inspector randomly selects 10 bulbs. Find, correct to three decimal places, the probability that:
  (i) exactly four bulbs are defective
 (ii) at least three bulbs are defective.

Solution

(i) P(exactly four defective bulbs)

$$= \binom{10}{4}(0.05)^4(0.95)^6 = 0.001 \qquad \text{(correct to three decimal places)}$$

(ii) We first calculate the probability of obtaining no defective bulbs, one defective bulb and two defective bulbs and then subtract this from 1.

P(no defective) + P(one defective) + P(two defective)

$$= \binom{10}{0}(0.05)^0(0.95)^{10} + \binom{10}{1}(0.05)^1(0.95)^9 + \binom{10}{2}(0.05)^2(0.95)^8$$

$$= 0.598736939 + 0.315124704 + 0.074634798$$

$$= 0.988 \qquad \text{(correct to three decimal places)}$$

$\therefore$ P(at least three defective bulbs) $= 1 - 0.988 = 0.012$

Example

A certain basketball player scores 60% of the free-throw shots she attempts. During a particular game, she gets six free throws.
  (i) What assumption(s) must be made in order to regard this as a sequence of Bernoulli trials?

(ii) Based on such assumption(s), find, correct to three decimal places, the probability that:

(a) she scores on exactly four of the six throws

(b) she scores for the second time on the fifth throw.

Solution

(i) Fixed number of trials, b.

Only two possible outcomes: she scores or she does not score.

Probability of success is constant: 0.6.

Trials are independent of each other.

(ii) (a) P(she scores exactly four of the six throws)

$$= \binom{6}{4}(0.6)^4(0.4)^2 = 0.311 \quad \text{(correct to three decimal places)}$$

(b) We need to calculate the probability of one success in the first four throws and then multiply this by the probability of success on the fifth throw.

$$P\text{(one success in the first four throws)} = \binom{4}{1}(0.6)(0.4)^3$$

P(success on the fifth throw) $= 0.6$

P(she scores for the second time on the fifth throw)

$$= \left[\binom{4}{1}(0.6)(0.4)^3\right] \times (0.6) = 0.092 \quad \text{(correct to three decimal places)}$$

Probability distributions

Expected value and standard deviation of a discrete random variable x

The mean value, μ, of the random variable x is called the **expected value** of x and is written as $E(x)$. The standard deviation is denoted by $\sigma(x)$.

$$\Sigma P(x) = 1$$

$$\boxed{\text{Mean} = \mu = E(x) = \Sigma x P(x)}$$

$$\boxed{\text{Standard deviation} = \sigma(x) = \sqrt{\Sigma(x - \mu)^2 P(x)}}$$

A game is considered fair if $E(x) = 0$.   (expected value $= 0$)

Example

A person plays a game that involves throwing five hoops at a peg.
The following table gives the probability distribution for the number of hoops that land on the peg.

x	0	1	2	3	4	5
P(x)	0·01	0·08	0·23	0·34	0·26	k

Find the:

(i) value of k (ii) mean   (iii) standard deviation, correct to two decimal places.

Solution

(i) $\Sigma P(x) = 1$ (sum of probabilities = 1)

$\therefore 0{\cdot}01 + 0{\cdot}08 + 0{\cdot}23 + 0{\cdot}34 + 0{\cdot}26 + k = 1$

$0{\cdot}92 + k = 1$

$k = 0{\cdot}08$

(ii) Mean $= \mu = \sum_{x=0}^{5} xP(x)$

$= 0{\cdot}01(0) + 0{\cdot}08(1) + 0{\cdot}23(2) + 0{\cdot}34(4) + 0{\cdot}26(4) + 0{\cdot}08(5)$

$= 0 + 0{\cdot}01 + 0{\cdot}46 + 1{\cdot}36 + 1{\cdot}04 + 0{\cdot}4 = 3$

(iii) Standard deviation $= \sqrt{\sum_{x=0}^{5} (x - \mu)^2 P(x)}$

$= \sqrt{(0-3)^2(0{\cdot}01) + (1-3)^2(0{\cdot}08) + (2-3)^2(0{\cdot}23) + (3-3)^2(0{\cdot}34) + (4-3)^2(0{\cdot}26) + (5-3)^2(0{\cdot}08)}$

$\therefore \sigma = \sqrt{0{\cdot}09 + 0{\cdot}32 + 0{\cdot}23 + 0 + 0{\cdot}26 + 0{\cdot}32} = \sqrt{1{\cdot}22} = 1{\cdot}10$

(or use a calculator)   (correct to two decimal places)

exam
Q

A charity got a licence to run a raffle. There is one grand prize of €20,000 and 20 additional prizes of €500. Tickets cost €10. When you read the small print, you discover that 10,000 tickets will be sold. Sheila bought one ticket and all the tickets were sold.

(i) Calculate the probability that Sheila wins

(a) the grand prize (b) a €500 prize (c) no prize.

(ii) Represent the situation with a probability distribution.

(iii) Calculate the expected value to

(a) the person who bought the ticket **(b)** the charity.

(iv) Is this a good bet? Justify your answer.

Solution

(i) **(a)** P(Sheila wins the €20,000 prize) $= \dfrac{1}{10,000}$

(b) P(Sheila wins a €500 prize) $= \dfrac{500}{10,000}$

(c) P(Sheila wins no prize) $= \dfrac{10,000 - 21}{10,000} = \dfrac{9,979}{10,000}$

(ii) Probability distribution

Prize, x	20,000	500	0
$P(x)$	$\dfrac{1}{10,000}$	$\dfrac{500}{10,000}$	$\dfrac{9,979}{10,000}$

(iii) **(a)** Expected value to the person who bought the ticket

Expected value $= \displaystyle\sum_{x=1}^{3} x\,P(x) - 10$

$= 20,000\left(\dfrac{1}{10,000}\right) + 500\left(\dfrac{500}{10,000}\right) + 0\left(\dfrac{9,979}{10,000}\right) - 10$

$= 2 + 1 + 0 - 10 = -7$ (a loss of €7)

Each person who pays €10 for a ticket has an expected return of €3. In other words, a loss of €7 for each ticket bought.

(b) The expected value to the charity is a profit of €7 for each €10 sold. Profit to the charity $= 10,000 \times 7 = €70,000$.

(iv) It does not look like a good bet. You buy a ticket for €10 and expect a return of €3. However, the money is going to charity. Thus, many people would not consider it to be a bad bet.

In a game a player tosses three fair coins. He wins €10 if three heads occur, €5 if two heads occur, a € if one head occurs and €2 if no heads occurs. It costs €4·20 to play each game.

(i) Represent this game with a probability distribution.

(ii) Find the value of a for which the game is fair.

(iii) Find his expected profit or loss if he played this game 120 times where $a = €1·40$.

Solution

(i) $P(H) = \frac{1}{2}$ and $P(T) = \frac{1}{2}$

Consider $(H + T)^3 = \binom{3}{0}H^3T^0 + \binom{3}{1}H^2T + \binom{3}{2}HT^2 + \binom{3}{3}H^0T^3$

$$= H^3 + 3H^2T + 3HT^2 + T^3$$

$$= \left(\frac{1}{2}\right)^3 + 3\left(\frac{1}{2}\right)^2\left(\frac{1}{2}\right) + 3\left(\frac{1}{2}\right)\left(\frac{1}{2}\right)^2 + \left(\frac{1}{2}\right)^3 \quad \left(\text{let } H = \tfrac{1}{2} \text{ and } T = \tfrac{1}{2}\right)$$

$$= \frac{1}{8} + \frac{3}{8} + \frac{3}{8} + \frac{1}{8}$$

$\therefore P(3H) = \dfrac{1}{8},\ P(2H) = \dfrac{3}{8},\ P(1H) = \dfrac{3}{8}$ and $P(OH) = \dfrac{1}{8}$

Probability distribution

No. of heads	0	1	2	3
x	2	a	5	10
$P(x)$	$\frac{1}{8}$	$\frac{3}{8}$	$\frac{3}{8}$	$\frac{1}{8}$

(ii) Given the game is fair

$\therefore \qquad\qquad E(x) - \text{payment to play} = 0$

$\therefore \qquad\qquad \displaystyle\sum_{x=0}^{3} xP(x) - 4\cdot2 = 0$

$\therefore 2\left(\dfrac{1}{8}\right) + a\left(\dfrac{3}{8}\right) + 5\left(\dfrac{3}{8}\right) + 10\left(\dfrac{1}{8}\right) - 4\cdot2 = 0$

(multiply each part by 8)

$$2 + 3a + 15 + 10 - 33\cdot6 = 0$$
$$3a - 6\cdot6 = 0$$
$$3a = 6\cdot6$$
$$a = 2\cdot2$$

Thus, $a = €2\cdot20$.

(iii) $a = 1\cdot4$

New probability distribution

No. of heads	0	1	2	3
x	2	1·4	5	10
$P(x)$	$\frac{1}{8}$	$\frac{3}{8}$	$\frac{3}{8}$	$\frac{1}{8}$

$E(x) - \text{payment to play}$

$$= 2\left(\frac{1}{8}\right) + 1\cdot4\left(\frac{3}{8}\right) + 5\left(\frac{3}{8}\right) + 10\left(\frac{1}{8}\right) - 4\cdot2$$

$$= \frac{2(1) + 3(1\cdot4) + 5(3) + 10(1)}{8} - 4\cdot2$$

$$= \frac{31\cdot2}{8} - 4\cdot2$$

$$= 3\cdot9 - 4\cdot2 = -0\cdot3$$

Thus, he would expect to lose 30c per game on average.

Thus, expected loss on 120 games = 120 × 30c = €36.

Bag A contains two red balls and three green balls. Two balls are chosen at random from the bag without replacement. Let X denote the number of red balls chosen. The following table shows the probability distribution for X.

X	0	1	2
$P(x)$	$\dfrac{3}{10}$	$\dfrac{6}{10}$	$\dfrac{1}{10}$

(i) Calculate $E(X)$, the mean number of red balls chosen.

(ii) Bag B contains four red balls and two green balls. Two balls are chosen at random from bag B.

  (a) Draw a tree diagram to represent the above information, including the probability of each event.

  (b) Hence, find the probability distribution for Y, where Y is the number of red balls chosen.

(iii) A standard die with six faces is rolled. If a 1 or 6 is obtained, two balls are chosen from bag A, otherwise two balls are chosen from bag B.

  (a) Calculate the probability that two red balls are chosen.

  (b) Given that two red balls are obtained, find the conditional probability that a 1 or 6 was rolled on the die.

Solution

(i) $E(x) = \Sigma x\,P(x)$

$$= 0\left(\frac{3}{10}\right) + 1\left(\frac{6}{10}\right) + 2\left(\frac{1}{10}\right) = \frac{8}{10} \text{ or } 0{\cdot}8$$

(ii) (a)

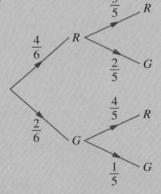

$R_1R_2 = \dfrac{4}{6} \times \dfrac{3}{5} = \dfrac{12}{30}$

$R_1G_2 = \dfrac{4}{6} \times \dfrac{2}{5} = \dfrac{8}{30}$

$G_1R_2 = \dfrac{2}{6} \times \dfrac{4}{5} = \dfrac{8}{30}$

$G_1G_1 = \dfrac{2}{6} \times \dfrac{1}{5} = \dfrac{2}{30}$

$\left(\text{Check: Sum of the probabilities} = \dfrac{12}{30} + \dfrac{8}{30} + \dfrac{8}{30} + \dfrac{2}{30} = 1\right)$

(b) $P(\text{no reds}) = \dfrac{2}{30}$

$P(\text{one red}) = \dfrac{8}{30} + \dfrac{8}{30} = \dfrac{16}{30}$

$P(\text{two reds}) = \dfrac{12}{30}$

Distribution for reds from bag B:

y	0	1	2
$P(y)$	$\dfrac{2}{30}$	$\dfrac{16}{30}$	$\dfrac{12}{30}$

(iii) (a) Die: 1, 2, 3, 4, 5, 6

$P(1 \text{ or } 6) = \dfrac{2}{6} = \dfrac{1}{3}$

$\therefore \quad P(A) = \dfrac{1}{3}$

$P(2, 3, 4 \text{ or } 6) = \dfrac{4}{6} = \dfrac{2}{3}$

$\therefore \quad P(B) = \dfrac{2}{3}$

$P(\text{two reds are chosen})$

$= P(\text{bag } A \text{ and then two reds}) \text{ or } P(\text{bag } B \text{ and then two reds})$

$= P(A) \times P(\text{two reds from } A) + P(B) \times P(\text{two reds from } B)$

$= \dfrac{1}{3} \times \dfrac{1}{10} \qquad\qquad + \dfrac{2}{3} \times \dfrac{12}{30}$

$= \dfrac{1}{30} \qquad\qquad\qquad + \dfrac{4}{15} = \dfrac{3}{10}$

(b) $P(1 \text{ or } 6 \mid R_1R_2) = \dfrac{P(1 \text{ or } 6 \text{ and } R_1R_2)}{P(R_1R_2)} = \dfrac{\dfrac{1}{30}}{\dfrac{3}{10}} = \dfrac{1}{9}$

10 Statistics I: Statistical Investigations

Introduction to statistics

Statistics deals with the collection, presentation, analysis and interpretation of data. Insurance (of people and property), which now dominates many aspects of our lives, utilises statistical methodology. Social scientists, psychologists, pollsters, medical researchers, governments and many others use statistical methodology to study behaviours of populations.

Statistics deals with events which have more than one possible outcome. If you buy a sandwich in the school canteen priced at €2·20 and offer the cashier a €5 note, you should receive €2·80 in change. This is not statistics, as there is (or should be) only one amount of change possible.

If the school canteen manager wishes to know how much students spend when visiting the canteen, this is statistics because different customers spend different amounts.

The quantity which varies (in this case, the amount of money) is called a **variable**.

A collection of variables are referred to as **data** in statistics.

An **observation** is the value of a variable for one particular element of the sample or population, for example your sandwich purchase.

A **data set** is all the observations of a particular variable for the elements of the sample, for example a complete list of the canteen transactions of all students from your class on a certain day.

Types of data

Data are a collection of facts. It can be numbers, measurements, descriptions or observations. On our course we consider **two** types of data: quantitative and qualitative.

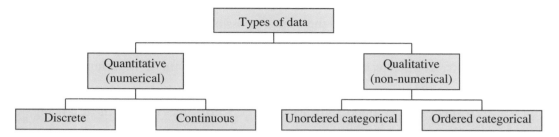

Quantitative data (numerical)	
Discrete numerical data	**Continuous numerical data**
Discrete numerical data are data which can only have certain values.	Continuous data are data which can take any numerical value within a certain range.
Examples are the number of students in a school, number of goals scored in a match and shoe sizes (including half-sizes).	Examples are time, weight, height, temperature, pressure and area. (Accuracy depends on the measuring device used.)

Qualitative data (non-numerical)	
Unordered categorical data	**Ordered categorical data**
Unordered categorical data are data that can be counted but only described in words without any order or ranking.	Ordered categorical data are data that can be counted but only described in words and have an order or ranking.
Examples are colours, names, type of car and gender (male or female).	Examples are examination grades, football divisions and income groups.

Note: Ordered categorical data are sometimes called **ordinal data**.

If a code is used to put data into a category, the data is called **nominal data**. The data are assigned a code in the form of a number or letter. The numbers or letters are simply labels. For example, males could be coded as 1 and females as 2. Marital status can be coded as M if married or S if single. Nominal data can be counted but not measured or ordered.

Note 1: Discrete variables take values which change in steps:

(0) (1) (2) (3)

The number of eggs a hen lays in a week can only take whole number values. **Discrete** means separate – there are no possible values in between.

Variables which are counted, such as the number of cars crossing a bridge in a minute, are discrete, but discrete variables are not limited to whole number values.

For example:
A student studies in blocks of 15 minutes. Study times include the following discrete values in hours:

$0, \dfrac{1}{4}, \dfrac{1}{2}, \dfrac{3}{4}, 1, 1\dfrac{1}{4}, 1\dfrac{1}{2}, \ldots$

Note 2: Continuous variables can take any value in an interval, such as the height of a child, length of a component or weight of an apple. Such variables are measured, not counted.

Width of Butterfly
6·8 cm

The butterfly could be 10 cm wide, 6.8 cm wide or any value in between. In practice, width is measured to a given accuracy, e.g. the nearest millimetre. Only certain values will be possible, but in theory there is no limit to the number of different possible widths.

key point

Sometimes variables which are strictly discrete may be treated as continuous. Money changes in steps of 1 cent and so is a discrete variable. However, if you are dealing with hundreds of euros, the steps are so small that it may be treated as a continuous variable.

Primary and secondary data

Primary data (first-hand data) are data that you collect yourself or are collected by someone under your direct supervision.

Secondary data (second-hand data) is data that have already been collected and made available from an external source such as newspapers, government departments, organisations or the Internet.

Primary and secondary data have their advantages and disadvantages.

Data	Advantages	Disadvantages
Primary	Know how it was obtained. Accuracy is also known.	Time consuming. Can be expensive.
Secondary	Easy and cheap to obtain.	Could be out of date. May have mistakes and be biased. Unknown source of collection.

Example

Classify each of the following variables in terms of data type (qualitative/quantitative, etc.).

   (i) Colours of flowers
  (ii) Number of bicycles owned by students in your school
 (iii) Ages of students in a primary school
  (iv) Volumes of contents of water bottles
   (v) Countries of birth of Irish citizens
  (vi) Number of strokes to complete a round of golf
 (vii) Proportions of faulty fridges in samples of size 50
(viii) Diameter of tennis balls
  (ix) Examination grades
   (x) Makes of TV in a salesroom

Solution

   (i) Qualitative – unordered categorical
  (ii) Quantitative – discrete numerical
 (iii) Quantitative – continuous numerical (but age in years is discrete)
  (iv) Quantitative – continuous numerical
   (v) Qualitative – unordered categorical
  (vi) Quantitative – discrete numerical
 (vii) Quantitative – discrete numerical
(viii) Quantitative – continuous numerical
  (ix) Qualitative – ordered categorical (ordinal)
   (x) Qualitative – unordered categorical

Populations and samples

To find out the average weight of men in Ireland we could, in theory, measure them all. In practice this would be almost impossible. Instead we can measure the weights of a sample.

Provided the sample is carefully chosen, we can obtain almost as much information from the sample as from measuring the weight of every man in Ireland.

In statistics we distinguish between a population and a sample.

> **key point**
>
> A **population** is all the possible data and a **sample** is part of the data.

The population is all the possible data

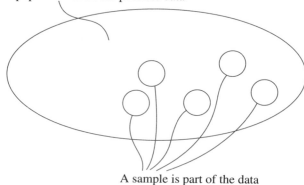

A sample is part of the data

> **key point**
>
> The difference between a population and a sample is of great importance.

Sampling is useful because it reduces the amount of data you need to collect and process. It also allows you to carry out a test without affecting all the population. For example, the contents of a sample of tubs of margarine, from a large batch, might be weighed to ensure that the actual contents matched that claimed on the label. Emptying the tubs to weigh the margarine makes them unsaleable, so it would be ridiculous to weigh the contents of the whole population of tubs.

Samples

A sample is a small part of the population selected for surveying. A random sample is a sample in which every member of the population has an equal chance of being selected and the selections are made independently. Notice this is sampling with replacement. When a population is very large compared with the size of the sample, the difference between sampling with and without replacement is negligible. Random sampling without replacement is considered to be a modification to random sampling with replacement.

Sampling methods

There are various ways of actually selecting a sample.

1. **Simple random sampling:** Sometimes called the lottery method, this is the best method (from a theoretical viewpoint) of selecting a truly random sample. All the

items in a population are given a number and pieces of paper, each with one number on it, are placed in a drum or hat. The numbers are selected one at a time until the required sample size is reached. This method is very tedious, particularly for very large populations. You must bear in mind that although the method of selection is free from personal bias, there is no guarantee that the resulting sample is unbiased. Sometimes a computer simulation may be used instead.

2. **Stratified sampling:** This method uses the natural divisions of a population, such as gender, age, weight, occupation or colour. These are the strata and they can be used to ensure all sections of the population are adequately represented in any sample. It is essential when using this method to know in advance the proportion of the population in each natural stratum and to take account of this when selecting the sample. The strata chosen must be readily determinable. They should be exhaustive and mutually exclusive (that is, covering the whole population and each item in the population belongs to one and only one stratum).

3. **Cluster sampling:** This consists of a list of groups of individuals rather than individuals themselves. A random sample of these groups or clusters is taken and then observations are made on every individual within these selected groups. Cluster samples are popular with biologists, agricultural scientists and geographers. Their technique is to cover the survey area with a grid of numbered squares. A random sample of the squares is taken and a complete study/investigation is made of the selected squares, whether it be plant species, incidence of disease or number of bacteria. It is preferable to divide the population/area into a large number of small clusters rather than a small number of large clusters.

4. **Quota sampling:** This method allows the interviewer a certain amount of discretion when collecting the data. Quotas for different sections of the population are set and the interviewer is allowed to select the sample according to these quotas, for example 30 teenagers, 15 female pensioners, 20 farmers, etc. Quota sampling is used to ensure that the sample contains members of the population in the desired proportions. As a result, the interviewer can be a source of bias, as only the views of those chosen by the interviewer are recorded. Quota sampling is an example of non-random sampling. Its main advantage is that it reduces survey time and cost.

exam focus

Candidates are expected to learn by rote the sampling methods described above.

An Irish sports journalist intends to write a book about the English football premiership. She will analyse all premiership matches in the season. For each match she records whether it is a home win, an away win or a draw. She also records, for each match, the total number of goals scored and the amount of time played before a goal is scored. Reference books showed that in the previous season the mean number of goals per game was 2·345. On the first weekend of the season she recorded the number of goals scored in each match and calculated the mean number of goals per match as 2·6.

After carefully reading the above passage, identify an example of:

- **(i)** a population
- **(ii)** a sample
- **(iii)** a qualitative variable
- **(iv)** a discrete variable
- **(v)** a continuous variable
- **(vi)** primary data
- **(vii)** secondary data.

Solution

(i) Populations mentioned in the passage will relate to all premiership matches played in the season and are either the results, the total number of goals or the amounts of time played before a goal is scored.

(ii) A sample would be the total number of goals scored in each match played, for example on the fourth weekend of the season.

(iii) A qualitative variable would be the result of matches: home win (H), away win (A), draw (D).

(iv) A discrete variable would be the number of goals scored in each match.

(v) A continuous variable would be the amount of time played before a goal is scored.

(vi) Primary data would be the data the journalist collected in that season.

(vii) Secondary data (obtained from a reference book) would be the mean number of goals per game in the previous season.

Sampling without bias

When you are selecting a sample, you need to avoid bias (anything which makes the sample unrepresentative). For example, if you want to estimate how often residents of Waterford visit the cinema in a year, it would be foolish to stand outside a cinema as the audience is coming out and ask people as they pass. This would give a biased sample, as all the people you ask would have been to the cinema at least once that year. You can avoid bias by taking a random sample.

Random sampling

> - For a sample to be random, every member of the population must have an equal chance of being selected.
> - A random sample chosen without replacement is called a simple random sample.

Suppose the population consists of the heights of 100 students in a college and you wish to take a sample of size 5. The students' names are arranged in alphabetical order and numbered 00 to 99. A number between 00 and 19 is selected by lottery methods. For example, place 20 equally sized balls numbered 00 to 19 in a bag and ask a blindfolded assistant to pick one out. This student and every 20th one thereafter are chosen and their heights measured. That is, if the number 13 is selected, then the students numbered 13, 33, 53, 73 and 93 are chosen. Every student would have an equal chance of being chosen. However, a sister and brother who were next to each other in the alphabetical list could never both be included in the same sample, so this is **not** a random sample.

Usually, if you decide to choose five students at random you intend to choose five different students and would not consider choosing the same student twice. This is known as sampling without replacement.

Example

An inspector tests every 80th assembly coming off a production line. Is this a good random sample of the assemblies? Justify your answer.

Solution

It is not a good random sample because, for example, two adjacent assemblies could not both be sampled.

However, it is a commonly used system in quality control.

> It is vital in the exam to have the ability and confidence to make a statement and back it up with a reason. The above example shows a system of selecting samples that is not strictly random but works very well in practice.

11 Statistics II: Central Tendency and Spread of Data

aims

☐ To know that mean, mode and median are all measures of average/central tendency and how to calculate them

☐ How to calculate range, interquartile range and standard deviation, which are all measures of spread

☐ To learn how to handle questions that link statistics with other sections of our Maths course and real-world/in-context questions

☐ To understand how to construct and apply statistical representation of data (e.g. histograms, stem and leaf plots)

☐ To describe distributions in terms of symmetry, skewness, etc. in calculating useful statistical information

☐ To understand and apply the concept of expected value

Averages

There are many types of averages. Three that we meet initially are called the mean, the mode and median. They are also known as measures of central tendency.

Mean

The mean is the proper name for what most people call the average.

key point

The mean of a set of values is defined as the sum of all the values divided by the number of values.

That is:

$$\text{Mean} = \frac{\text{Sum of all the values}}{\text{Number of values}}$$

The formula is often written as: $\mu = \dfrac{\Sigma x}{n}$ (see booklet of formulae and tables page 33)

Mode

key point

The mode of a set of items is the item that occurs most often. If there are no repeated items, then the mode does not exist.

Median

When the values are arranged in ascending or descending order of size, then the median is the middle value. If the number of values is even, then the median is the average of the two middle values.

Note: Half the values lie below the median and half the values lie above the median. The median is also called the second quartile (Q_2).

A measure of spread

The range is the difference between the highest data value and the lowest data value.

Range = highest value − lowest value

The interquartile range is more useful than the range, but is more complicated to calculate.

Here is a diagram to help clarify the situation.

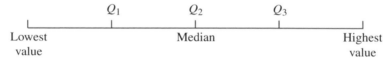

The median (Q_2) is the value that subdivides the ordered data into two halves.

The quartiles $(Q_1$ and $Q_3)$ subdivide the data into quarters.

The interquartile range is upper quartile minus lower quartile = $Q_3 - Q_1$.

Example

Four numbers are:

$$2, 13, x, 5$$

   (i) If their mode is 13, find the value of x.
  (ii) If their mean is 7, find the value of x.
 (iii) If their range is 12, find the possible values of x.
 (iv) If their median is 7, find the value of x.

Solution

(i) Mode $= 13 \Rightarrow$ the most common number in the list $2, 13, x, 5$ is 13.

$\Rightarrow x = 13$

(ii) Mean $= \mu = \dfrac{2 + 13 + x + 5}{4} = 7$

$$20 + x = 28$$
$$x = 8$$

(iii) If x is not an end value, then the range $= 13 - 2 = 11 \neq 12$. Hence, we need to consider two (ascending) cases.

$2, 5, 13, x$	$x, 2, 5, 13$
Range $= x - 2$	Range $= 13 - x$
$12 = x - 2$	$12 = 13 - x$
$14 = x$	$x = 1$

(iv) The median of four numbers is the average of the two middle numbers when the numbers are arranged in ascending (or descending) order.

Now x cannot be the smallest number because $x, 2, 5, 13$ has

$$\text{median} = \frac{2 + 5}{2} = 3\frac{1}{2} \neq 7.$$

Similarly, x cannot be the largest number because $2, 5, 13, x$ has

$$\text{median} = \frac{5 + 13}{2} = 9 \neq 7.$$

Thus, either $2, x, 5, 13$ $\boxed{\text{or}}$ $2, 5, x, 13$ is possible.

Then $\dfrac{5 + x}{2} = 7$

$$5 + x = 14$$
$$x = 9$$

Example

45 students in a class each recorded the number of whole minutes, x, spent doing experiments on Monday. The total of the results is $\displaystyle\sum_{i=1}^{45} x_i = 2{,}232$.

(i) Find the mean number of minutes the students spent doing experiments on Monday.

(ii) Two new students joined the class and reported that they spent 37 minutes and 34 minutes, respectively. Calculate the new mean including these two students.

Solution

(i) Mean $= \dfrac{\text{Total}}{\text{Number of students}}$

$= \dfrac{\sum\limits_{i=1}^{45} x_i}{45} = \dfrac{2{,}232}{45} = 49{\cdot}6 \text{ mins}$

(ii) Total for 47 students $= 2{,}232 + 37 + 34 = 2{,}303$

New mean $= \dfrac{2{,}303}{47} = 49$

Variability of data

Each of these sets of numbers has a mean of 4, but the spread of each set is different:

(a) 4, 4, 4, 4, 4   (b) 1, 3, $3\frac{1}{2}$, 4·2, 8·3   (c) −196, −49, 25, 66, 174

There is no variability in set (a), while the numbers in set (c) are much more spread out than in set (b).

key point

We have three ways of measuring the variability or spread of a distribution: the **range**, the **interquartile range** and the **standard deviation**.
We already met the range and the interquartile range.

The standard deviation (σ)

The standard deviation (σ, pronounced 'sigma') is an important and useful measure of spread. It gives a measure of the deviations from the mean, μ. It is calculated using all the values in the distribution.

To calculate σ:

- For each reading x, calculate $x - \mu$, its deviation from the mean.
- Square this deviation to give $(x - \mu)^2$. Note that irrespective of whether the deviation was positive or negative, this is now positive.
- Find $\Sigma(x - \mu)^2$, the sum of all these values.
- Find the average by dividing the sum by n, the number of readings. This gives $\dfrac{\Sigma(x - \mu)^2}{n}$.
- Finally, take the positive square root of $\dfrac{\Sigma(x - \mu)^2}{n}$ to obtain the standard deviation, σ.

The standard deviation, σ, of a set of n numbers with mean μ is given by:

$$\sigma = \sqrt{\frac{\Sigma(x - \mu)^2}{n}}$$ (see the formulae and tables booklet page 33)

Hence, the standard deviation for:

(a) $4, 4, 4, 4, 4$ is calculated to find $\sigma = 0$

(b) $1, 3, 3\frac{1}{2}, 4{\cdot}2, 8{\cdot}3$ is calculated to find $\sigma = 2{\cdot}4$

(c) $-196, -49, 25, 66, 174$ is calculated to find $\sigma = 123{\cdot}3$

key point

Set **(a)**, with data not spread out about the mean, has $\sigma = 0$, while set **(c)** has a much higher standard deviation than set **(b)**, confirming that **(c)** is much more spread about the mean.

Properties of the standard deviation

- σ measures spread about the mean and should be used only when the mean is chosen as the measure of centre.

- $\sigma = 0$ only when there is *no spread*. This happens only when all observations have the same value. Otherwise, $\sigma > 0$. As the observations become more spread out about their mean, σ gets larger. We can say that the higher the standard deviation, the greater the variability in the data.

- σ, like the mean, μ, is affected by extreme values.

- The square root in the formula for $\sigma = \sqrt{\dfrac{\Sigma(x - \mu)^2}{n}}$ ensures that the x-values and the standard deviation are in the same units.

exam focus

You can use your calculator to calculate the standard deviation, σ. Calculator instructions can be found at the end of this book.

exam Q

The first five terms of an arithmetic sequence are e, f, 17, g, h. Calculate the mean of these five numbers. Justify your answer.

Solution

For an arithmetic sequence we can write:

$a - 2d \qquad a - d \qquad a \qquad a + d \qquad a + 2d$

To get the mean of five numbers we use $\frac{\Sigma x}{5}$:

$$= \frac{(a - 2d) + (a - d) + (a) + (a + d) + (a + 2d)}{5}$$

$$= \frac{5a}{5}$$

$$= a$$

$\therefore$ Mean $= a = $ The middle term in the arithmetic sequence. $e, f, 17, g, h$ is the given arithmetic sequence.

$\therefore$ Mean $=$ middle term $= 17$.

The above work is my justification.

key point

Sequences are covered under Chapter 9 Pattern, Sequences and Series in LSMS Leaving Cert Higher Level Paper 1.

exam Q

The first four terms of a geometric sequence are:

x	6	9	y

(i) Find the value of x.

(ii) Find the value of the common ratio of the sequence.

(iii) Hence, find:

  (a) the mean

  (b) the standard deviation of $\{x, 6, 9, y\}$ correct to one decimal place.

Solution

(i) In a geometric sequence:

Common ratio $= \dfrac{\text{2nd term}}{\text{1st term}} = \dfrac{\text{3rd term}}{\text{2nd term}} = \dfrac{\text{4th term}}{\text{3rd term}} = \cdots\cdots$

Gives $\dfrac{6}{x} = \dfrac{9}{6} = \dfrac{y}{9}$

Now $\dfrac{6}{x} = \dfrac{9}{6}$

$(6)(6) = (9)(x)$ (multiply both sides by $6x$)

$36 = 9x$

$4 = x$

(ii) Common ratio $= \dfrac{6}{x} = \dfrac{6}{4} = \dfrac{3}{2}$

(iii) Now $y = \dfrac{3}{2}(9)$

$\Rightarrow y = 13\cdot5$

(a) Mean of $\{4, 6, 9, 13\cdot5\}$

$= \dfrac{4 + 6 + 9 + 13\cdot5}{4}$

$= 8\cdot125$

$= 8\cdot1$ (correct to one decimal place)

(b) Standard deviation of $\{4, 6, 9, 13\cdot5\}$

$\sigma = \sqrt{\dfrac{\Sigma(x - \mu)^2}{n}}$

$\sigma = \sqrt{\dfrac{(4 - 8\cdot1)^2 + (6 - 8\cdot1)^2 + (9 - 8\cdot1)^2 + (13\cdot5 - 8\cdot1)^2}{4}}$

$= 3\cdot577$

$\sigma = 3\cdot6$ (correct to one decimal place)

Alternatively, you may use your calculator to enter the data and find $\sigma = 3\cdot6$.

In the previous exam questions, basic knowledge of arithmetic and geometric sequence are required before you can successfully tackle the statistics question. This type of question, which involves cross-over of topics, features prominently in the exam.

Histogram

A histogram is often used to display information contained in a frequency distribution. It is similar to a bar chart with no gaps between the bars, and the two are often confused. The essential characteristic of a histogram is that the **area of each rectangle represents the frequency**, and the sum of the areas of the rectangles is equal to the sum of the frequencies.

Bar charts can only represent discrete data, while histograms can represent discrete or continuous data.

A group of 80 students is randomly divided into two classes, each containing 40 students. Both classes take the same examination. The results are given below in a frequency table.

Marks	Class P Number of students	Class Q Number of students
0–10	0	3
10–20	13	20
20–30	22	7
30–40	4	6
40–50	1	4

[**Note:** 0–10 means 0 marks or more but less than 10 marks, etc.]

(i) Draw separate histograms for Class P and Class Q.

(ii) Compare the features of the two histograms. Use them to describe two similarities or differences between Class P and Class Q.

(iii) **Use your graphs** and show your method clearly to estimate the median mark for each class.

(iv) Students scoring 15 marks or less must take the class and the examination again. **Use your graphs** and show your method clearly to estimate how many students, in total, must take the class and the examination again.

(v) Would you advise these students to attempt to be in Class P or Class Q? Give a reason.

(vi) By calculating μ_P, the mean mark for Class P, and σ_P, the standard deviation for Class P, estimate the number of students in the interval

$$(\mu_P - \sigma_P, \mu_P + \sigma_P).$$

Solution

(i)

Class P

Marks	0–10	10–20	20–30	30–40	40–50
Number of students	0	13	22	4	1

Class Q

Marks	0–10	10–20	20–30	30–40	40–50
Number of students	3	20	7	6	4

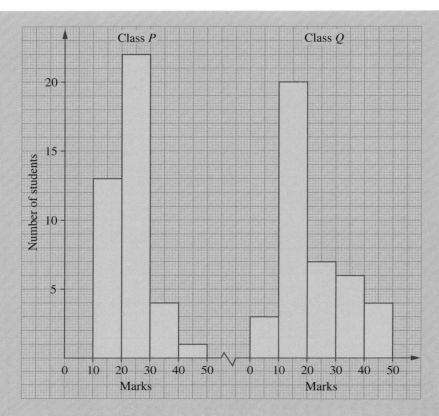

(ii) From the histograms:

The marks for Class Q are more spread out.

Class P seems to have better results overall.

(iii) 40 is the total number of students in each class.

The median is thus associated with the 20th student.

Hence:

For Class P

0 + 13 + (7 out of 22) $\longrightarrow$
Median Class P

Thus, the median is $\frac{7}{22}$ along the interval 20–30.

This interval is 10 wide

$\left(\frac{7}{22}\right)(10) = \frac{70}{22} = 3\cdot2$

∴ Median is 20 + 3·2 = 23·2

For Class Q

3 + (17 out of 20) $\longrightarrow$
Median Class Q

Thus, the median is $\frac{17}{20}$ along the interval 10–20.

This interval is 10 wide

$\left(\frac{17}{20}\right)(10) = 8\cdot5$

∴ Median is 10 + 8·5 = 18·5

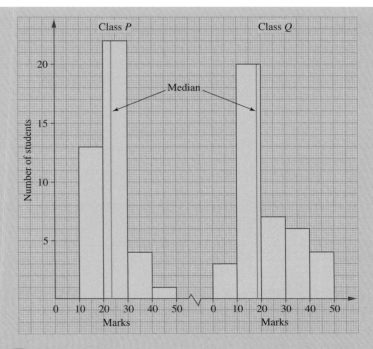

The median line (in red) divides each histogram so that there are 20 students represented on both sides of each median.

(iv)

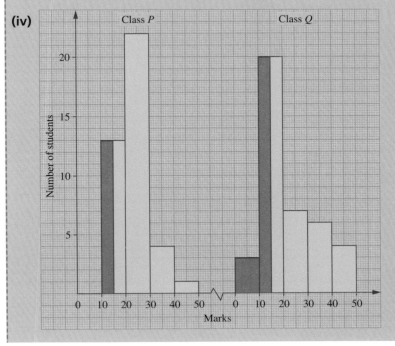

Note: The red section indicates the students who must take the class and the examination again.

< 15 marks in Class P

Corresponds to half the number of students in the [10–20] marks section = $\frac{1}{2}(13) = 6\frac{1}{2}$,

i.e. 6 or 7 students.

< 15 marks in Class Q

Corresponds to all students in the [0–10] marks section plus half the number of students in the [10–20] marks section

$$= 3 + \frac{1}{2}(20)$$

$$= 3 + 10$$

$$= 13 \text{ students}$$

(v) Would advise students to be in Class P, as fewer students from P have to take the examination again.

(vi) The frequency distribution for Class P with the mid-interval values for marks is:

Marks	5	15	25	35	45
Number of students	0	13	22	4	1

By calculator $\mu_P = 23 \cdot 25$ and $\sigma_P = 7$.

Now $(\mu_P - \sigma_P, \mu_P + \sigma_P) = (23\cdot25 - 7, 23\cdot25 + 7)$

$$= (16\cdot25, 30\cdot25)$$

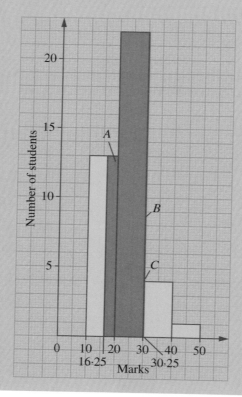

Estimate of number of students = Area of sections $A + B + C$

$$= \left(\frac{20 - 16{\cdot}25}{10}\right)(13) + (22) + \left(\frac{30{\cdot}25 - 30}{10}\right)(4)$$

$$= 4{\cdot}875 \qquad\qquad + 22 \quad + 0{\cdot}1$$
$$= 5 \qquad\qquad\quad + 22 \quad + 0 \qquad \text{(estimate)}$$

Answer: 27 students between $(\mu - \sigma, \mu + \sigma)$.

Distributions and shapes of histograms

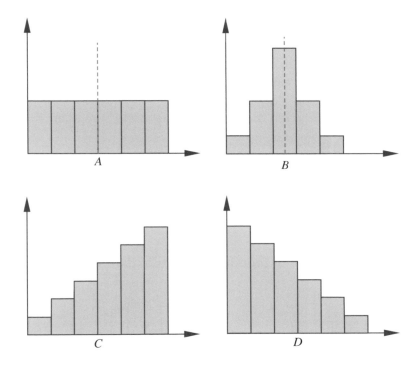

Histograms come in many different shapes. Above we have four histograms, all with different shapes:

A has uniform distribution and is symmetric (balanced).
B has a symmetric shape.
C has no axis of symmetry. It is negatively skewed, that is, there is a tail at the negative end of the distribution.
D has no axis of symmetry and is positively skewed.

The diagram below shows a skewed frequency distribution. Vertical lines have been drawn through the mean, mode and median. Identify which is which by inserting the relevant letter in the spaces below.

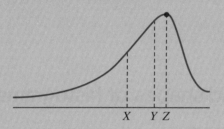

Mean =   Mode =   Median =

Solution

The mode (most common) is associated with the highest point on the curve $\Rightarrow$ mode = Z.

The median (middle) is between the mean and the mode $\Rightarrow$ median = Y.

Finally, the mean = X.

The shapes of the histograms of four different sets of data are shown below.

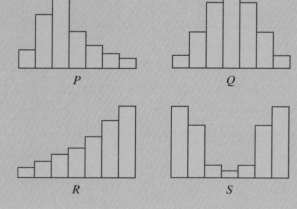

(i) Complete the table below, indicating whether the statement is correct (✓) or incorrect (×) with respect to each data set.

	P	Q	R	S
The data are skewed to the left				
The data are skewed to the right				
The mean is equal to the median				
The mean is greater than the median				
There is a single mode				

(ii) Assume that the four histograms are drawn on the same scale. State which of them has the largest standard deviation. Justify your answer.

Solution

(i)

	P	Q	R	S
The data are skewed to the left	×	×	✓	×
The data are skewed to the right	✓	×	×	×
The mean is equal to the median	×	✓	×	✓
The mean is greater than the median*	✓	×	×	×
There is a single mode	✓	✓	✓	×

*Note in Q and S the mean is equal to the median.

(ii) S has the largest deviation because a lot of the data are far from the mean.

Stem and leaf diagrams

Histograms provide an easy to understand summary of the distribution of data. However, they do not show the values themselves. For this we need a stem and leaf diagram.

Example

The ordered stem and leaf plot shows the times taken by 24 students to complete an exercise.

Stem	Leaf
0	6 8 8 9
1	1 4 5 7 7 8
2	0 1 1 3 4 5 5 6
3	2 2 6 6 7 8

Key: $0\,|\,9 = 9$ minutes

Use this stem and leaf plot to calculate the following.

(i) The range   (ii) The median   (iii) The lower quartile

(iv) The upper quartile   (v) The interquartile range

Solution

(i) Range = largest value − smallest value = $38 - 6 = 32$ minutes.

(ii) The median mark (Q_2) is the time value halfway through the distribution. The halfway value is between the 12th and 13th values.

$$= \tfrac{1}{2}[21 + 21] = 21$$

∴ The median = 21 minutes.

(iii) The lower quartile (Q_1) is the value one-quarter of the way through the distribution. This one-quarter value is between the 6th and 7th values.

$$= \tfrac{1}{2}[14 + 15] = 14\tfrac{1}{2}$$

∴ The lower quartile (Q_1) = $14\tfrac{1}{2}$ minutes.

(iv) The upper quartile (Q_3) is the value three-quarters of the way through the distribution. This three-quarters value is between the 18th and 19th values.

$$= \tfrac{1}{2}[26 + 32] = 29$$

∴ The upper quartile (Q_3) = 29 minutes.

(v) The interquartile range

$$= Q_3 - Q_1 = 29 - 14\tfrac{1}{2} = 14\tfrac{1}{2} \text{ minutes.}$$

Always use an **ordered** stem and leaf diagram.

An educator believes that Project Maths methods will help Leaving Certificate students improve their maths grades. She arranges for a Leaving Cert class of 21 students to take part in Project Maths methods for a one-year period. A control class of 24 Leaving Cert students follow the traditional maths methods. At the end of the year a maths test is given to all students. The results in percentages are given on the ordered back-to-back stem and leaf plots.

4	3	1 9
5 4	4	2 2
8 7 6 2	5	1 3 7 9 9 9
8 6 6 3 3 1	6	0 6 2 8
7 6 3 2 2	7	1 1 3 5
8 5 4	8	1 2 8

Write down four errors in the above ordered back-to-back stem and leaf plots.

exam focus

Although it is not used in this example, back-to-back stem and leaf plots allow us to compare two data sets.

Solution

Error 1: The plot does not indicate which group is traditional and which is Project Maths.

Error 2: The right-hand line

	6	0 6 2 8

is not ordered. It should read:

	6	0 2 6 8

Error 3: There are 21 readings on both sides of the plot. One side should have 24 readings.

Error 4: No key on either side.

Right-hand side 7|3 = 73%

Left-hand side 6|5 = 56%

The population of Ireland is ageing, though less rapidly than in other developed countries. Here is an ordered stem and leaf plot of the percents of residents aged 65 and over in the 32 counties according to a recent census. The stems are whole percents and the leaves are tenths of a percent.

5	9
6	
7	
8	
9	6 7
10	6
11	0 2 3 6 7
12	0 1 1 1 4 4 5 7 9
13	1 2 3 3 3 8 8
14	0 7 8 9
15	3 6
16	
17	6

(i) There are two outliers: County Leitrim has the highest percent of older residents and County Dublin has the lowest. What are the percentages for these two counties?

(ii) Ignoring Leitrim and Dublin, describe the shape and spread of this distribution.

Solution

(i) 17.6% for Leitrim
5.9% for Dublin

(ii) The mean is located at the *central stem* of the stem and leaf plot (or the central rectangle of the histogram), as in the diagram below. Since the mean is at the centre, the shape is symmetrical.

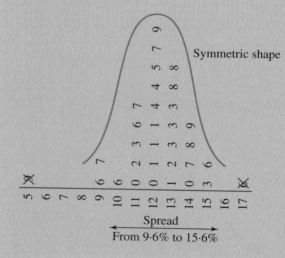

Spread
From 9·6% to 15·6%

Outliers are values that are noticeably more extreme than the majority of scores.

Expected value (see Chapter 9)

The mean value, μ, of a set of numbers, R, can also be called the expected value of R and written as $E(R)$.

The expected value does not have to be one of the original elements in R.

(i) Calculate the mean, μ, and the standard deviation of the population of the four numbers 2, 3, 7, 8.

(ii) A sample of three numbers is to be drawn at random from this population (without replacement). Let $\overline{X}$ be the mean of this sample. List all such possible samples and calculate the value of $\overline{X}$ in each case.

Hence, find the expected value of $\overline{X}$ and the standard deviation of $\overline{X}$.

(iii) Explain how your work in **(i)** and **(ii)** satisfied the formula $\mu = E(\overline{X})$.

(iv) If the samples were drawn with replacement, would you expect the standard deviation of $\overline{X}$ to be smaller than, equal to or larger than the previous value? Give reasons.

Solution

(i) Mean $= \mu = \dfrac{2 + 3 + 7 + 8}{4} = \dfrac{20}{4} = 5$

Standard deviation $= \sigma = 2{\cdot}5$ using a calculator.

(ii) Possible samples $\Rightarrow \{2, 3, 7\} \ \{2, 3, 8\} \ \{2, 7, 8\} \ \{3, 7, 8\}$

Finding the mean of each sample gives $\overline{X} \Rightarrow 4; \dfrac{13}{3}; \dfrac{17}{3}; 6.$

The expected value of $\overline{X}$

$= \dfrac{4 + \dfrac{13}{3} + \dfrac{17}{3} + 6}{4} = \dfrac{20}{4} = 5$

The standard deviation of $\overline{X}$
$= \sigma(\overline{X}) = 0{\cdot}85$, using a calculator.

key point

$E(\overline{X})$ = mean of values for $\overline{X}$

(iii) From part **(i)**, $\mu = 5$.

From part **(ii)**, the expected value of $\overline{X} = E(\overline{X}) = 5$

$\therefore$ By comparison $\mu = E(\overline{X})$.

(iv) Samples drawn with replacement from 2, 3, 7, 8 three at a time

All the same: {2, 2, 2} {3, 3, 3} {7, 7, 7} {8, 8, 8}

All different: {2, 3, 7} {2, 3, 8} {2, 7, 8} {3, 7, 8}

Exactly two the same: {2, 2, 3} {2, 2, 7} {2, 2, 8} {3, 3, 2} {3, 3, 7} {3, 3, 8}

{7, 7, 2} {7, 7, 3} {7, 7, 8} {8, 8, 2} {8, 8, 3} {8, 8, 7}

This gives 20 different sets with the following $\bar{X}$:

2, 3, 7, 8, 4, $\frac{13}{3}$, $\frac{17}{3}$, 6, $\frac{7}{3}$, $\frac{11}{3}$, 4, $\frac{8}{3}$, $\frac{13}{3}$, $\frac{14}{3}$, $\frac{16}{3}$, $\frac{17}{3}$, $\frac{22}{3}$, 6, $\frac{19}{3}$, $\frac{23}{3}$.

These twenty $\bar{X}$ numbers are more spread out than the four $\bar{X}$ numbers from **(ii)**.

∴ Expect the standard deviation of the samples drawn with replacement to be larger than the previous standard deviation in part **(ii)**.

Candidates would not be expected to write out the sample in **(iv)** above. This is done to show you exactly what's going on. The final three lines in **(iv)** are all the examiner requires.

12 Statistics III: Scatter Graphs and Correlation

aims
- ☐ Know where to find (and apply) the relevant statistical information in the booklet of formulae and tables
- ☐ Know how to describe correlation in words and numbers
- ☐ Know how to draw and interpret scatter plots
- ☐ Know how to find $(\bar{x}, \bar{y})$ and construct a line of best fit
- ☐ Know how and when to apply the numbers μ, σ, r found by using the calculator and work with $y = a + bx$ as the line of best fit

Correlation

Scatter plots (graphs)

Is the number of cigarettes smoked by an individual related to the age of their death?

Are your overall Leaving Certificate results related to the number of hours you spend at your part-time job?

To look at the relationship between two sets of quantitative data, we plot the points on a graph (similar to x-axis/y-axis). Data that come in pairs are called **bivariate data**.

key point

Scatter plots are used whenever we are examining possible relationships between two variables (bivariate data).

When analysing scatter plots, we use the word 'correlation' to describe the strength of the linear relationship between two variables.

Scatter plot patterns

Here are three scatter diagrams that are typical of what we meet.

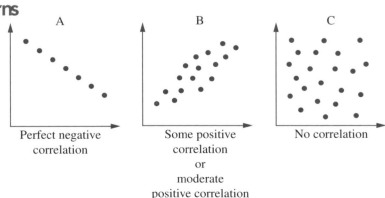

A — Perfect negative correlation

B — Some positive correlation or moderate positive correlation

C — No correlation

We get negative correlation where increasing values of one variable are associated with generally decreasing values of the other variable (case A above).

We get positive correlation where increasing values of one variable are associated with generally increasing values of the other variable (case B above).

We have no correlation when the points are randomly and widely spaced out (case C above).

Correlation measures the strength of the linear association between two quantitative variables. Before using correlation, check the following.

1. Are both variables quantitative?
2. Check the scatter plot for evidence of 'straightness', i.e. can you visualise a straight line passing through the plot and representing the relationship? We call this the line of best fit by eye.
3. Check for outliers and extreme values (stragglers). Outliers are very important and always deserve special attention. Outliers can make a weak correlation look strong or can hide a strong correlation.

Example

The Type Fast secretarial training agency has a new computer software spreadsheet package. The agency investigates the number of hours it takes people of varying ages to reach a level of proficiency using this package. Fifteen individuals are tested and the results are summarised in the table below.

Age (x)	32	40	21	45	24	19	17	21	27	54	33	37	23	45	18
Time (in hours) (y)	10	12	8	15	7	8	6	9	11	16	t	13	9	17	5

(i) Given the mean time taken was 10·6 hours, calculate the value of t.
(ii) Plot the data on a scatter plot.
(iii) Comment on the strength and direction of the correlation of the scatter plot in (ii).

Solution

(i) $\dfrac{10 + 12 + 8 + 15 + 7 + 8 + 6 + 9 + 11 + 16 + t + 13 + 9 + 17 + 5}{15}$

$\Rightarrow \dfrac{146 + t}{15} = 10 \cdot 6$

$146 + t = 159$

$t = 13$

(ii)

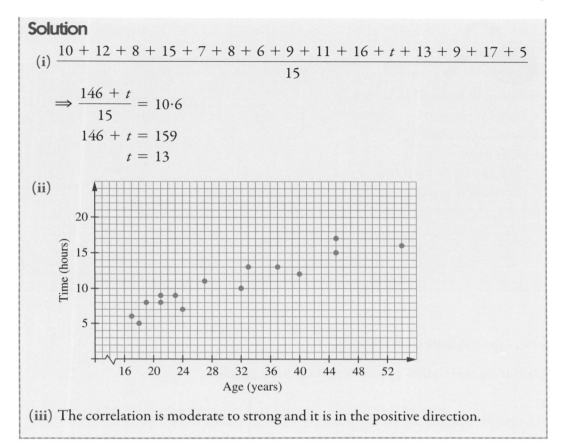

(iii) The correlation is moderate to strong and it is in the positive direction.

Interpreting scatter plots and calculating r, the correlation coefficient

We use scatter plots to help understand data, but now we have to understand scatter plots.

Interpreting a scatter diagram is often the easiest way for you to decide whether correlation exists. Correlation means that there is a linear relationship between the two variables. This could mean that the points lie on a straight line, but it is much more likely to mean that they are scattered about a straight line.

We need to be familiar with:

- Correlation + or −
- How to calculate r
- $(\bar{x}, \bar{y})$ point
- Line of best fit written as $y = a + bx$
- Correlation versus causality
- Outliers, see circled point in the diagram

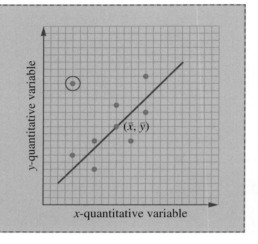

The correlation coefficient, r

Measuring correlation of scatter plots (scatter graphs)

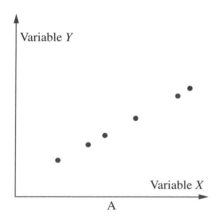

A

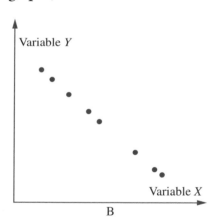

B

The points on scatter graph A are in a straight line. In this case we say there is **perfect positive correlation** between the two variables, X and Y.

We use the letter r to represent the correlation. We say that $r = 1$ when we have perfect positive correlation.

The points on scatter graph B are in a straight line. In this case we say there is **perfect negative correlation** between the two variables, X and Y.

We say that $r = -1$ when we have perfect negative correlation.

How the correlation, r, measures the direction and strength of a linear association:

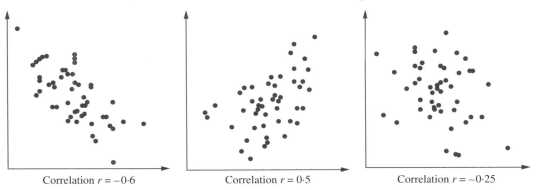

| Correlation $r = -0.6$ | Correlation $r = 0.5$ | Correlation $r = -0.25$ |

To calculate the correlation coefficient

> **key point**
>
> It is always true that $-1 \leq r \leq 1$.

The first step is to establish that a linear (straight line) relationship exists between two variables, x and y. To do this, we draw and then examine a scatter plot.

When we see a straight line relationship on the scatter plot, we then proceed to measure the strength of the relationship between the two variables.

There are several ways of doing this. The most common measure is the **Pearson product moment correlation coefficient**, otherwise known as the correlation coefficient, r.

Usually we estimate the value of the population correlation coefficient using samples from the populations. That is, when looking for a correlation between the age of a car and the distance travelled, we do not consider every car, only the samples of cars given in the question.

This sample correlation coefficient is called r and it measures the linearity of the relationship between x and y for a sample of n points.

$(x_1, y_1), (x_2, y_2), (x_3, y_3) \ldots \ldots (x_n, y_n)$

What r is not

- r is not the slope of the line of best fit.
- r is not resistant. This means r is strongly affected by outliers.
- r is never a value above 1.
- r is never a value below -1.
- r does not describe curved relationships.
- An r value of $+0.58$ is not better than an r value of -0.75. Do not assume a positive value of r is good or a negative value of r is not good.

exam focus

How r is calculated is not examined on this course.

However, it is important that candidates can find r using a calculator. This is a skill you should learn. The instructions for using a calculator are at the back of this book.

If you cannot use your calculator on exam day, then you decide by observation from the given scatter plot whether r is negative or positive and write down your best guess for r, correct to one decimal place.

Example

Snow White and the seven dwarfs have their heights and weights measured. On the scatter plot, Snow White is represented by W.

(i) From the plot, write down the bivariate data (couple) for Snow White.

(ii) Calculate the correlation coefficient for the seven dwarfs by reading the bivariate data from the plot and entering the data on your calculator.

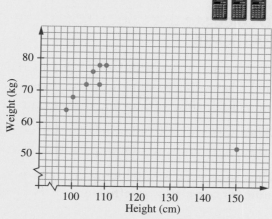

(iii) Calculate the value of r when Snow White is included.

(iv) Write a comment on the difference between the two values of r and the extent to which the outlier dominates the correlation value.

Solution

(i) $W = (150, 52)$

(ii) and (iii)

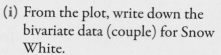

Height (cm)	110	108	100	108	106	104	98	150
Weight (kg)	78	72	68	78	76	72	64	52

For seven dwarfs, $r = 0.92$.

For seven dwarfs and Snow White, $r = -0.68$.

(iv) For the seven dwarfs, $r = 0.92$ indicates an extremely strong positive correlation for the bivariate data. (The taller dwarfs are heavier.)

When Snow White is included, $r = -0.68$, which indicates a moderate negative correlation for the data.

This clearly shows a massive domination of the correlation by the inclusion of Snow White.

In this case, Snow White is an outlier, that is, a value that is unusual (does not fit with) compared to the rest of the data.

If the sample is a large random sample, an extreme value (outlier) will not greatly alter the size of the correlation. However, if the sample is a small one, as above, an extreme data point can have a disproportionately large effect.

Example

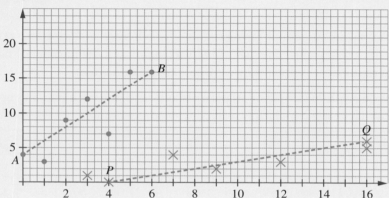

(i) Calculate the correlation coefficient, r, for the bivariate data.

$(0, 4) = A$, $(1, 3)(2, 9)(3, 12)(4, 7)(5, 16)$ and $(6, 16) = B$ on the graph, marked with dots.

(ii) Calculate the slope of the line AB.

(iii) Hence or otherwise, calculate the correlation coefficient, r, for the bivariate data.

$(4, 0) = P$, $(3, 1)(9, 2)(12, 3)(7, 4)(16, 5)$ and $(16, 6) = Q$ on the graph, marked with Xs.

(iv) Calculate the slope of the line PQ.

Solution

(i) Calculator $r = 0 \cdot 86$

(ii) Slope of $AB = \dfrac{y_2 - y_1}{x_2 - x_1}$

$(x_1, y_1) = (0, 4)$

$(x_2, y_2) = (6, 16)$

Slope of $AB = \dfrac{16 - 4}{6 - 0} = \dfrac{12}{6} = 2$

(iii) Calculator $r = 0 \cdot 86$

You should notice that the correlation coefficient r for both data sets AB and PQ is the same.

(iv) Slope of $PQ = \dfrac{y_2 - y_1}{x_2 - x_1}$

$(x_1, y_1) = (4, 0)$

$(x_2, y_2) = (16, 6)$

Slope of $PQ = \dfrac{6 - 0}{16 - 4} = \dfrac{6}{12} = \dfrac{1}{2}$

It is vital to notice that:

- slope $\neq r$
- slope of $AB \neq$ slope PQ.

Example

A consultant orthopaedic surgeon is trying to establish whether a relationship exists between the age of patients who have had hip replacements and the number of days, following the operation, after which they were able to walk unaided.

He chooses a simple random sample of 10 patients and tabulates each patient's age and the number of days after which they walked without assistance.

Age of patients in years, x	69	61	54	75	58	71	65	61	50	56
Number of days, y	50	45	40	50	42	45	46	37	32	33

(i) (a) Find $\bar{x}$, the mean age of the patients.

   (b) Find $\bar{y}$, the mean number of days to walking unaided.

(ii) Represent the data, including the point $(\bar{x}, \bar{y})$, on a scatter plot. Hence, draw a line of best fit for the bivariate data.

(iii) Describe the correlation. Calculate the correlation coefficient, r, for

   (a) the 10 patients (b) the 10 patients and the point $(\bar{x}, \bar{y})$.

(iv) Compare the answers to (iii) (a) and (b).

(v) Using your calculator or otherwise, write an equation for a line of best fit in the form $y = a + bx$ where $a, b \in R$ and both constants are correct to two decimal places.

Solution

(i) (a) $\bar{x} = \dfrac{69 + 61 + 54 + 75 + 58 + 71 + 65 + 61 + 50 + 56}{10} = \dfrac{620}{10} = 62$

   (b) $\bar{y} = \dfrac{50 + 45 + 40 + 50 + 42 + 45 + 46 + 37 + 32 + 33}{10} = \dfrac{420}{10} = 42$

(ii) Scatter plot

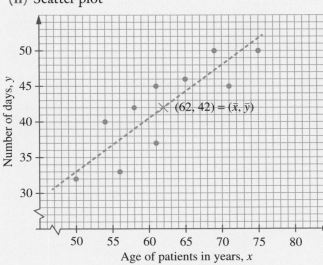

(iii) The correlation seems to be positive and very strong. (The value of r, written below, confirms a very strong positive correlation.)

Enter the data on your calculator to find:

(a) $r = 0.849117632$

(b) $r = 0.849117632$

(iv) See the key point.

(v) Method 1

In the same way we found r, the calculator provides values $a = -0.53$ and $b = 0.69$ (here, both are rounded correct to two decimal places).

With the values, $y = a + bx$ becomes $y = -0.53 + 0.69x$.

From our work we have:

Days to walking unaided $= -0.53 + 0.69$ (age of patient)

The scatter plot shows that this line of best fit fits the data well for the age range 50 to 75 years. Below or above that range, the plot is of limited use, e.g. age 0 years $\Rightarrow -0.53$ days to walking unaided!

However, the slope $b = 0.69$ tells us that the time to walking unaided after the operation increases by 0.69 days for every added year of age within the age range 50 to 75 years.

Method 2

Select the point $(\bar{x}, \bar{y}) = (62, 42)$ and one other suitable point on the line of best fit, say $(50, 33)$.

This suitable point should be on the line of best fit, as far from $(\bar{x}, \bar{y})$ as possible but inside the range of the given date,

e.g. not $(80, 55)$ nor $(45, 29)$.

$$\text{Slope} = \frac{42 - 33}{62 - 50} = \frac{9}{12} = 0.75$$

Equation given by:

$$y - y_1 = \text{slope}(x - x_1)$$
$$y - 42 = 0.75(x - 62)$$
$$y - 42 = 0.75x - 46.5$$
$$y = 0.75x - 4.5$$

key point

Method 1 and Method 2 give similar slopes, but they give different intercepts, reinforcing the idea that the correlation breaks down at extreme values.

exam Q

(i) Explain, with the aid of an example, what is meant by the statement 'correlation does not imply causality'.

(ii) The data given in the table below and represented in the scatter diagram are pairs of observations of the variables x and y.

x	1	2	3	4	5	6
y	11	15	17	17	15	11

(a) Calculate the correlation coefficient.

(b) What kind of relationship, if any, do the observed data suggest exists between x and y?

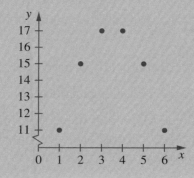

Solution

(i) Attracta said, 'We had a fire in our house recently. Five firemen and one fire engine were called to deal with it. The insurance company paid the claim of €17,000 for the damage.' Her friend Noreen replied, 'We had a fire in our house last year. Eighteen firemen and two fire engines were called to deal with it. The insurance company paid the claim of €235,000 for the damage. Those firemen caused a frightful mess.'

Correlation between two variables does not automatically mean that one causes the other, e.g. as the number of firemen fighting the fire rises, so does the insurance claim.

The size, strength, duration and ferocity of the fire increases the size of the claim, not the firemen. However, the number of firemen present is related to the dimensions of the fire.

A positive correlation between two variables does not mean that one is necessarily causing the other. For example, in a primary school there might be a correlation between reading ability and shoe size, but big feet don't make you read better and reading doesn't make your feet grow! In this case, both variables are connected to age – a 'confounding factor'.

(ii) (a) Calculator $\Rightarrow r = 0$

    (b) No (linear) relationship.

    The relationship may be quadratic. This type of relationship is not on the course.

13 Statistics IV: The Normal Curve, z-Scores, Hypothesis Testing and Simulation

aims

- ☐ To be familiar with the empirical rule and normal curves
- ☐ To read the z-tables (tables provided in the back of this book) for forward and backward cases
- ☐ How to apply the normal curve/z-scores to in-context questions
- ☐ To know how to calculate a margin of error
- ☐ Be able to construct a confidence interval for a statistical investigation
- ☐ Understand and handle the idea of the 95% confidence level
- ☐ To use the standard error and via simulations to apply the central limit theorem
- ☐ Gain the skills to apply the above knowledge to in-context exam questions

The normal distribution

Many continuous variables, which occur naturally, have a shape like this.

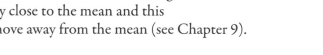

This is called a normal distribution. It has a high probability density close to the mean and this decreases as you move away from the mean (see Chapter 9).

key point

The main features of normal distribution are that it is:

- bell shaped
- symmetrical (about the mean)
- the total area under the curve is 1.

Examples of variables which are likely to follow a normal distribution are:

- the lengths of leaves from oak trees
- the times taken by 10-year-old girls to run 100 m
- the heights of adult males in Ireland
- the widths of car doors coming off a production line.

Empirical rule (68%, 95% or almost all) for the normal curve

For many large populations, the **empirical rule** provides an estimate of the approximate percentage of observations that are contained within one, two or three standard deviations of the mean.

- Approximately **68%** of the observations are in the interval $\mu \pm 1\sigma$.
- Approximately **95%** of the observations are in the interval $\mu \pm 2\sigma$.
- Almost all of the observations are in the interval $\mu \pm 3\sigma$.

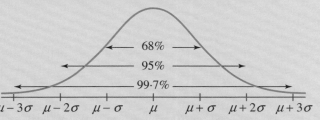

exam
focus

It is vital for candidates to know the empirical rule for the normal curve.

Example

Marks obtained on a national test (Test A1) are normally distributed with a mean of 100 and a standard deviation of 16.

(i) (a) Draw a large, neat diagram showing the distribution of marks. Label the points which show marks of 100, 116, 132 and 148.

(b) What percentage of the students who took Test A1 obtained marks greater than 116 ?

(c) What is the probability that a randomly selected student who took the test obtained a mark of less than 68?

(d) What are the end points of the interval which has its centre at the mean and within which 95% of the marks lie?

(ii) A new national test (Test B1) was constructed to have marks ranging from 100 to 250 and to be normally distributed for this range.

(a) What is the mean mark on Test B1?

(b) What is the median mark?

(c) If 84% of students obtained marks of less than 196 on Test B1, estimate the standard deviation of marks for this test.

Solution

(i) (a)

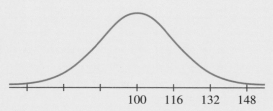

100   116   132   148

(b) We make use of this graph illustrating the empirical rule.

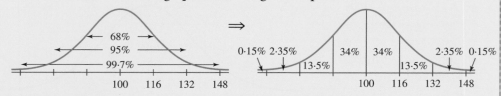

By observation from the above graph, the percentage of students scoring greater than 116 marks $= 13{\cdot}5\% + 2{\cdot}35\% + 0{\cdot}15\% = 16\%$.

$\therefore$ Approximately 16% of students scored greater than 116 marks.

> **key point**
>
> The normal curve is symmetric about the mean.

(c)

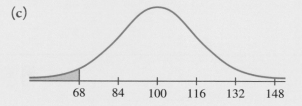

68   84   100   116   132   148

Approximately 2·5% of randomly selected students will obtain a mark of less than 68.

(d)

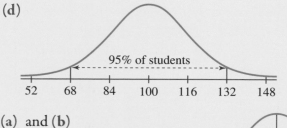

95% of students

52   68   84   100   116   132   148

End points of interval are [68, 132].

(ii) (a) and (b)

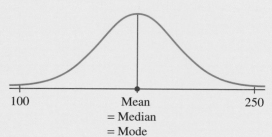

100   Mean   250
            = Median
            = Mode

Mean mark on Test B1 $= \dfrac{100 + 250}{2} = 175 = \mu.$

Median mark = mean mark for normal distribution = 175.

(c)

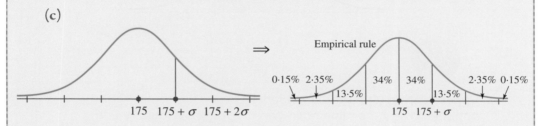

$\Rightarrow$ Empirical rule

0·15% 2·35%   34%   34%   2·35% 0·15%

13·5%   13·5%

175 175 + σ 175 + 2σ   175 175 + σ

Notice: $0 \cdot 15\% + 2.35 + 13 \cdot 5 + 34 + 34 = 84\%$
From the empirical rule, 84% of students score $< \mu + \sigma$.
$\therefore \mu + \sigma = 196 \Rightarrow 175 + \sigma = 196$ Answer: $\sigma = 21$

Example

A certain type of vegetable has a weight which follows a normal distribution with mean 450 grams and a standard deviation of 50 grams.

(i) In a load of 3,000 of these vegetables, calculate the expected number with a weight greater than 525 grams.

(ii) Find the upper quartile of the distribution.

Solution

(i) Use $z = \dfrac{x - \mu}{\sigma}$ where $x = 525$, $\mu = 450$ and $\sigma = 50$. (see booklet of formulae and tables page 34)

$\therefore z = \dfrac{525 - 450}{50} = \dfrac{75}{50} = 1 \cdot 5$

Now $P(x > 525) = P(z > 1 \cdot 5)$

$= 1 - 0 \cdot 9332$

$= 0 \cdot 0668$

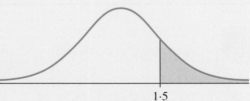

1·5

From 3,000 of these vegetables, we expect $(3,000)(0 \cdot 0668) = 200 \cdot 4$, that is, 200 vegetables, with a weight greater than 525 grams.

exam focus

Expected number of outcomes

= (Probability of the event) × (The number of trials)

(ii)

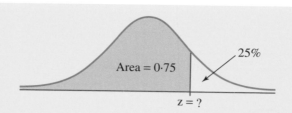

z = ?

key
point

Upper quartile (Q_3) is the boundary between the top 25% of the population and the remainder. We refer to this boundary as the 75th percentile.

The z-score associated with an area of 0·75 can be found in the booklet of formulae and tables page 36 or the extract here.

z	0·00	0·01	0·02	0·03	0·04	0·05	0·06	0·07	0·08	0·09
0·6	0·7257	·7291	·7324	·7357	·7389	·7422	·7454	·7486	·7517	·7549

The z-score associated with an area of 0·75 is given in the tables as either z = 0·67 or z = 0·68.

To ensure the top 25% of the population, we take z = 0·68.

Then $z = \dfrac{x - \mu}{\sigma}$ becomes $0·68 = \dfrac{x - 450}{50}$. (multiply both sides by 50)

$$34 = x - 450 \Rightarrow 34 + 450 = x$$

$\therefore$ 484 grams is the upper quartile boundary.

exam
Q

The heights of certain plants are normally distributed. The plants are classified into three categories.

The shortest 12·92% are in category A.

The tallest 10·38% are in category C.

All the other plants are in category B, with heights between k cm and t cm.

(i) Complete the following diagram to represent this information.

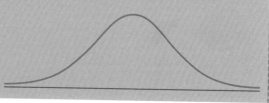

(ii) Using $z = \dfrac{x - \mu}{\sigma}$, write down a formula for the value of:

    (a) z_1, associated with category A

    (b) z_2, associated with category C.

(iii) Use the tables to calculate the value of **(a)** z_1 **(b)** z_2.

(iv) Given that the mean height is 6·84 cm and the standard deviation is 0·25 cm, find the value of k and of t.

Solution

(i)

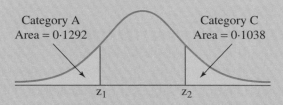

Category A
Area = 0·1292
z_1

Category C
Area = 0·1038
z_2

(ii) (a) $z_1 = \dfrac{k - 6\cdot84}{0\cdot25}$ **(b)** $z_2 = \dfrac{t - 6\cdot84}{0\cdot25}$

(iii) (a) Calculate z_1.   **(b)** Calculate z_2.

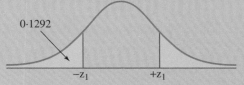

0·1292
$-z_1$ $+z_1$

Because normal curve is symmetric

Note: $1 - 0\cdot1292 = 0\cdot8708$

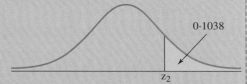

0·1038
z_2

Note: $1 - 0\cdot1038 = 0\cdot8962$

Extract from normal distribution tables

z	0·00	0·01	0·02	0·03	0·04	0·05	0·06	0·07	0·08
1.1	0·8643	·8665	·8686	(·8708)	·8729	·8749	·8770	·8790	·8810
1.2	0·8849	·8869	·8888	·8907	·8925	·8944	(·8962)	·8980	·8997

The above extract from the tables gives us the two values for z:

    $z_1 = -1\cdot13$ $z_2 = 1\cdot26$

(iv)   Now $z_1 = \dfrac{k - 6\cdot84}{0\cdot25}$ Now $z_2 = \dfrac{t - 6\cdot84}{0\cdot25}$

   Becomes $-1\cdot13 = \dfrac{k - 6\cdot84}{0\cdot25}$ Becomes $1\cdot26 = \dfrac{t - 6\cdot84}{0\cdot25}$

       $-0\cdot2825 = k - 6\cdot84$ $0\cdot315 = t - 6\cdot84$

         $6\cdot5575 = k$ $7\cdot155 = t$

Some data are reported as a set of scores and are presented in the table below. The scores are experimental observations, rounded off to the nearest integer.

Score	6	7	8	9	10	11	12	13	14
Frequency	2	5	13	16	20	18	15	7	4

(i) Calculate the mean score.

(ii) Calculate the standard deviation of the scores.

(iii) A research assistant thinks that the scores have a normal distribution with parameters μ and σ. What values of μ and σ are suggested by the data?

(iv) To help in forming an opinion about the suitability of the normal model, compare the observed percentage of scores less than or equal to 8 with an appropriate probability.

(v) To help in forming an opinion about the suitability of the normal model, compare the observed percentage of scores greater than 12 with an appropriate probability.

(vi) Does the normal model seem plausible in light of your answers for **(iv)** and **(v)**?

Solution

(i) Mean = $\mu = \dfrac{\Sigma \text{ scores}}{\Sigma \text{ frequencies}} = \dfrac{1{,}020}{100} = 10{\cdot}2$

(ii) Standard deviation = $\sigma = \sqrt{\dfrac{\Sigma f(x - \mu)^2}{100}} = 1{\cdot}86$

(iii) $\mu = 10{\cdot}2$ and $\sigma = 1{\cdot}86$ are suggested

(iv) By observation from the table:

$P(x \leq 8) = \dfrac{2 + 5 + 13}{100} = 0{\cdot}2 = 20\%$

Using the normal curve model:

$P(x \leq 8) = P\left(z \leq \dfrac{8 - 10{\cdot}2}{1{\cdot}8}\right) = P(z \leq -1{\cdot}18)$

By symmetry:

$P(z \leq -1{\cdot}18) = P(z \geq 1{\cdot}18)$

$= 1 - P(z \leq 1{\cdot}18)$

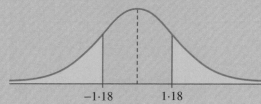

Extract from normal distribution tables

z	0·00	0·01	0·02	0·03	0·04	0·05	0·06	0·07	0·08	0·09
1.1	0·8643	·8665	·8686	·8708	·8729	·8749	·8770	·8790	(·8810)	·8830

$\therefore P(z \le -1·18) = 1 - 0·8810 = 0·1190 = 12\%$

(v) By observation, from the table $P(x \ge 12) = \dfrac{15 + 7 + 4}{100} = 0·26 = 26\%$

Using the normal curve model:

$P(x \ge 12) = P\left(z \ge \dfrac{12 - 10·2}{1·86}\right) = P(z \ge 0·97) = 1 - P(z \le 0·97)$

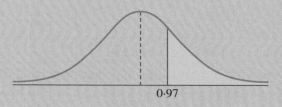

0·97

Extract from normal distribution tables

z	0·00	0·01	0·02	0·03	0·04	0·05	0·06	0·07	0·08	0·09
0.9	0·8159	·8186	·8212	·8238	·8264	·8289	·8315	(·8340)	·8365	·8389

$\therefore P(x \ge 12) = 1 - P(z \le 0·97) = 1 - 0·8340 = 0·166 = 17\%$

(vi) From **(iv)** $\left.\begin{array}{l} \text{By observation } P(x \le 8) = 20\% \\ \text{By normal model } P(x \le 8) = 12\% \end{array}\right\}$ (very different answers)

In **(v)** $\left.\begin{array}{l} \text{By observation } P(x \ge 12) = 26\% \\ \text{By normal model } P(x \ge 12) = 17\% \end{array}\right\}$ (very different answers)

Conclusion: The normal model does not seem plausible in light of the very different answers found by (the more reliable) observations from the table.

Hypothesis testing

A hypothesis is a statement (or theory) whose truth has yet to be proven or disproven. Examples of hypotheses:

- More than half the population is satisfied with EU membership.
- Drinking fizzy drinks causes tooth decay.
- The age of marriage has increased over the past 20 years.

> **NULL HYPOTHESIS**
> The statement being tested in a test of significance is called the **null hypothesis.** The test of significance is designed to assess the strength of the evidence against the null hypothesis. Usually the null hypothesis is a statement of no effect or no difference. We abbreviate 'null hypothesis' as H_0.

Statistics help to make decisions

We can use statistics to accept or reject claims.

1. Is global temperature increasing?
   The null hypothesis, H_0, is that global temperature is not increasing, i.e. no difference in temperature. The alternative hypothesis, H_A, is that global temperature is increasing.

2. Is a new drug effective at treating HIV/AIDS?
   The null hypothesis, H_0, is that the new drug is not effective.
   The alternative hypothesis, H_A, is that the new drug is effective.

3. Is a survey on left-handed people biased if it indicates 24% of people are left handed?
   The null hypothesis, H_0, is that 24% of people are left handed, i.e. survey not biased.
   The alternative hypothesis, H_A, is that the survey is biased.

Often the people investigating the data hope to reject H_0. They hope:
 (i) their new drug is better than the old one

or

 (ii) the new ad campaign is better than the original

or

(iii) the new machine is better than the existing one.

However, in statistics, it is essential that our attitude is one of skepticism. Until we are convinced otherwise, we accept H_0. In other words, we cling to the idea that there is no change, no improvement, no deterioration, no effect.

The reasoning behind hypothesis testing is that we usually prefer to think about getting things right rather than getting them wrong. A similar logic applies in trials by jury, where the defendant is considered innocent until it is shown otherwise.

Margin of error

We now look at the real business of statistics: to save people time and money! None of us want to do unnecessary work and statistics can tell us exactly how lazy we can afford to be.

Our problem is that the collections of stuff in the world are so large, it's very difficult to get the information we want, e.g. voting populations, what percentage favours each candidate, what is the average length of sardines to fit in a can, what proportion of TVs will be defective?

We could answer questions of this type by measuring every sardine in the world (say) and doing some calculations. This method is not for statisticians: they want the easy way out.

Statisticians take **samples**. A sample is a relatively small subset of the total population, e.g. pollsters at election time.

An obvious question is: How big a sample do we have to take to get a meaningful result?

The answer turns out to involve $\dfrac{1}{\sqrt{n}}$, where n is the number of items in the sample.

key point

In statistics, the margin of error is a number that represents the accuracy of a survey.

The margin of error is denoted by E. On our course, the margin of error, at the 95% level of confidence, is given by:

key point

Margin of error $= E = \dfrac{1}{\sqrt{n}}$ where n is the size of the sample

If $n = 100$: $\quad E = \dfrac{1}{\sqrt{100}} = 0{\cdot}1 = 10\%$

If $n = 400$: $\quad E = \dfrac{1}{\sqrt{400}} = 0{\cdot}05 = 5\%$

If $n = 1{,}000$: $\quad E = \dfrac{1}{\sqrt{1{,}000}} = 0{\cdot}0316227766 = 3{\cdot}16\%$ (correct to two decimal places)

If $n = 10{,}000$: $\quad E = \dfrac{1}{\sqrt{10{,}000}} = 0{\cdot}01 = 1\%$

There is an inverse relationship between the sample size, n, and the margin of error, E. The smaller the sample size, the larger the margin of error. However, there are diminishing returns. Going from a sample size of 100 to a sample size of 1,000, a tenfold increase, will decrease the margin of error from 10% to 3·16%. Going from a sample size of 1,000 to a sample size of 10,000, also a tenfold increase, will decrease the margin of error from 3·16% to 1%.

Note: One factor that generally has little effect on the margin of error is the population size. For example, a sample size of 100 in a population of 10,000 will have almost the same margin of error as a sample size of 100 in a population of 1,000,000.

Example

At the 95% confidence level, calculate the sample size, n, to have a margin of error of:

(i) 1·25%   (ii) 3%

Solution

$$\frac{1}{\sqrt{n}} = \text{margin of error}$$

(i)   1·25% = 0·0125

$$\frac{1}{\sqrt{n}} = 0·0125$$

$$1 = 0·0125\sqrt{n}$$

(multiply both sides by $\sqrt{n}$)

$$\frac{1}{0·0125} = \sqrt{n}$$

(divide both sides by 0·0125)

$$\frac{1}{(0·0125)^2} = n$$

(square both sides)

$$6,400 = n$$

(ii)   3% = 0·03

$$\frac{1}{\sqrt{n}} = 0·03$$

$$1 = 0·03\sqrt{n}$$

(multiply both sides by $\sqrt{n}$)

$$\frac{1}{0·03} = \sqrt{n}$$

(divide both sides by 0·03)

$$\frac{1}{(0·03)^2} = n$$

(square both sides)

$$1111·111111 = n$$

$$1,112 = n$$

Note: Always use the next whole number value of n, not to the nearest whole number.

The estimated proportion plus or minus its margin of error is called a **confidence interval** for the true proportion. The 95% confidence for a proportion is given by:

key point

sample proportion − margin of error ≤ true proportion ≤ sample proportion + margin of error

$$\hat{p} - \frac{1}{\sqrt{n}} \le p \le \hat{p} + \frac{1}{\sqrt{n}}$$

Where n is the sample size, p is the population proportion and $\hat{p}$ is the sample proportion.

We can state with 95% confidence that the true population, p, lies inside this interval. What this means is that if the same population was surveyed on numerous occasions and the confidence interval was calculated, then about 95% of these confidence intervals would contain the true proportion and about 5% of these confidence intervals would not contain the true proportion.

The end points of the 95% confidence are given by $\hat{p} \pm \dfrac{1}{\sqrt{n}}$.

Example

(i) A survey was carried out on 1,600 randomly selected people and the result was that 960 were in favour of holding an election now. At the 95% confidence level, calculate:

  (a) the margin of error

  (b) the confidence interval for the proportion of the people that want an election now.

(ii) Four weeks later, a similar survey was carried out on 1,200 randomly selected people to see if there was a change in support for an election. The result was that 696 are now in favour of a change of government.

The null hypothesis, H_0, is there is no change in the support for the government. At the 95% level of confidence for this second survey, would you accept the null hypothesis? Give a reason for your answer.

Solution

(i) (a) At the 95% level of confidence, the margin of error $= \dfrac{1}{\sqrt{n}} = \dfrac{1}{\sqrt{1,600}} = 0.025$

$$= 2.5\%$$

(b) The sample proportion $= \hat{p} = \frac{960}{1,600} = 0.6 = 60\%$

The 95% confidence interval for the proportion of people, p, who want an election now is:

$$\hat{p} - \frac{1}{\sqrt{n}} \leq p \leq \hat{p} + \frac{1}{\sqrt{n}}$$

$$0.6 - 0.025 \leq p \leq 0.6 + 0.025$$

$$0.575 \leq p \leq 0.625$$

$$57.5\% \leq p \leq 62.5\%$$

Thus, the 95% confidence level for the proportion of people who want an election now is between 57·5% and 62·5%, inclusive.

Answers can also be given in brackets: [0·575, 0·625] or [57·5%, 62·5%].

(ii) Null hypothesis $= H_0 =$ there is no change in support for an election now. In the second survey, $\hat{p} = \frac{696}{1,200} = 0.58$ (58%).

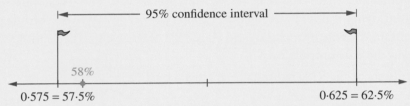

58% is inside the 95% confidence interval in the first survey. Thus, we do not reject the null hypothesis.

key point

If the second sample proportion was outside the 95% confidence interval, 57·5 to 62·5, we would reject the null hypothesis.

exam focus

What does '95% confidence' really mean?

What do we mean when we say we have 95% confidence that our interval contains the randomly selected value? Formally, what we mean is that '95% of randomly selected values will be captured/fall into the confidence interval'. This is correct, but somewhat long winded, so we usually say 'we are 95% confident that the (randomly) selected value lies in our interval.'

Our uncertainty is about whether the particular (randomly) selected value is one of the successful ones or one of the 5% that falls outside the interval.

When working with levels of confidence (or levels of significance), statisticians can use percentages ambiguously. In particular, the 5% level of significance and the 95% level of confidence mean the same thing. That is to say, 5% of the time outside the confidence interval or 95% of the time inside the confidence interval.

$2\frac{1}{2}\%$ 95% inside $2\frac{1}{2}\%$

The normal curve and confidence intervals

Given data that is approximately normal and using the mean (μ) and standard deviation (σ), we can calculate the z-score for each and every data point x, using $z = \dfrac{x - \mu}{\sigma}$.

The empirical rule tells us that about 95% of all randomly selected data points will be within $\pm 2\sigma$ from μ or within ± 2 from 0. That is to say, if we reach out 2 standard deviations on both sides from the mean, we are sure to 'trap' 95% of the data.

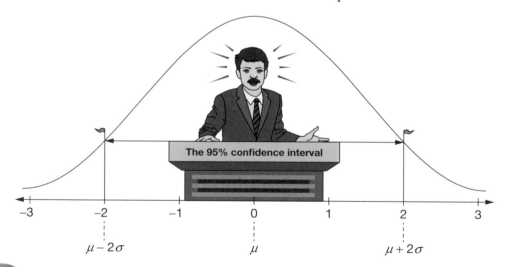

The 95% confidence interval

$\mu - 2\sigma$ μ $\mu + 2\sigma$

exam Q

A scientific expedition discovers a large colony of birds. The weights x kg of a random sample of 200 of these birds are measured and the following results obtained:

$$\sum x = 224 \cdot 4, \quad \sum (x - \mu)^2 = 5 \cdot 823$$

(i) Calculate unbiased estimates of the mean, μ, and the standard deviation, σ, of the weights of these birds.

(ii) Find a 95% confidence interval for an individual bird.

(iii) State, with a reason, whether or not your answer in part **(ii)** requires the assumption that the weights are normally distributed.

Solution

(i) Mean $= \mu = \dfrac{\Sigma x}{n} = \dfrac{224 \cdot 4}{200} = 1 \cdot 122$ kg

Standard deviation $= \sigma = \sqrt{\dfrac{\Sigma(x - \mu)^2}{n}}$

$$= \sqrt{\dfrac{5 \cdot 823}{200}} = 0 \cdot 171 \text{ kg}$$

(ii) Method 1: Using the empirical rule

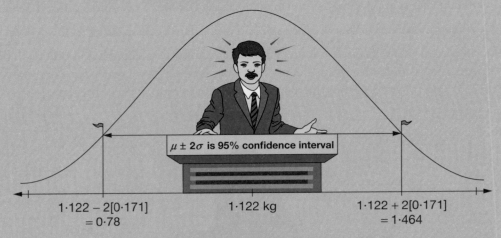

$\mu \pm 2\sigma$ is 95% confidence interval

$1 \cdot 122 - 2[0 \cdot 171]$	1·122 kg	$1 \cdot 122 + 2[0 \cdot 171]$
$= 0 \cdot 78$		$= 1 \cdot 464$

95% confidence interval given by mean ± 2 standard deviations

$= 1 \cdot 122 - 2[0 \cdot 171]$ to $1 \cdot 122 + 2[0 \cdot 171]$

$= 0 \cdot 78$ kg to $1 \cdot 464$ kg

Method 2: Using normal distribution tables

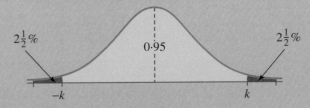

To find the value of k, use the normal curve distribution with μ and σ from part **(i)**.

Notice the area of $z \le k$ is given by $2\frac{1}{2}\% + 95\% = 97\frac{1}{2}\%$.

Hence, use $P(z \le k) = 97\frac{1}{2}\% = 0 \cdot 975$ to find the value of k.

The extract from the tables $\Rightarrow k = 1{\cdot}96$

z	0·00	0·01	0·02	0·03	0·04	0·05	0·06
1.9	0·9713	·9719	·9726	·9732	·9738	·9744	·9750

$\therefore\ z = \dfrac{x - \mu}{\sigma}$ becomes

$$\pm 1{\cdot}96 = \frac{x - 1{\cdot}122}{0{\cdot}171}$$

$\pm 0{\cdot}335 = x - 1{\cdot}122$

$1{\cdot}122 \pm 0{\cdot}335 = x$

$1{\cdot}122 - 0{\cdot}335 = 0{\cdot}787$ kg and $1{\cdot}122 + 0{\cdot}335 = 1{\cdot}457$ kg

$\Rightarrow 95\%$ confidence interval $= [0{\cdot}787, 1{\cdot}457]$

key point

The empirical rule interval [0·78, 1·464] is slightly wider than the interval [0·787, 1·457] found using the normal distribution tables. Using the tables gives a more accurate result.

(iii) Yes, the answer requires the assumption that the weights are normally distributed in order to use the tables or apply the empirical rule.

exam Q

25 students each measure and record a particular angle of elevation, in degrees, each using his or her own home-made clinometer.
The results are as follows:

24	20	22	15	70
15	16	15	16	15
18	16	21	21	73
16	20	12	18	20
18	18	14	22	18

(i) Find what you consider to be the best estimate of the true value of the angle. Explain your reasoning.

(ii) Based on previous experience, a teacher has claimed that in these circumstances, half of all students will measure the angle correctly to within two degrees. Taking these students to be a simple random sample, and assuming the true value of the angle is the one you calculated in part **(i)**, is there sufficient evidence to reject the teacher's claim at the 5% level of significance?

Solution

(i) There are several methods that will lead to success in this question.

One method is to draw an ordered stem and leaf plot and use the median as the best estimate.

Median value = 18
Good idea because median
is not influenced by outliers.

1	2	4	5	5	5	5	6	6	6	6	8	8	⑧	8	8
2	0	0	0	1	1	2	2	4							
3															
4															
5															
6															
7	0	3													

Key $2|1 = 21°$

Note: Two students seem to have very atypical answers. However, on reflection they may have simply misread the clinometer, reading the complementary angle:

i.e. $90 - 70 = 20°$ and $90 - 73 = 17°$

(ii) Taking 18° from **(i)**, then 12 students measured correctly to within 2°. You may check this yourself by counting from the stem and leaf plot.

How many measured between 18 ± 2?

How many measured between 16 and 20 inclusive?

Answer $= \frac{12}{25} = 48\%$ of students.

We must know the 95% margin of error for a sample of size $n = 25$ is given by

$$\frac{1}{\sqrt{n}} = \frac{1}{\sqrt{25}} = \frac{1}{5} = 0.2 = 20\%.$$

In the question, the teacher claims that half (= 50%) of the students will measure the angle correctly to within 2°.

Since the margin of error is $\pm 20\%$, we expect $50\% \pm 20\%$ of students to measure correctly. That is, from 30% to 70% of students to measure correctly. Since 48% 'fits' between 30% to 70% $\Rightarrow$ there is not significant evidence to reject the teacher's claim.

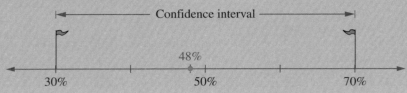

exam focus

The majority of candidates could not do **(ii)** on the previous page in a recent exam.

Central limit theorem

The central limit theorem was postulated in the 18th century by Abraham De Moivre, then in the 19th century Simon Laplace expanded on De Moivre's findings.
The theorem states: If we take random samples of size n from a population of mean μ and standard deviation σ, then as n gets large, $\bar{x}$, the sample mean, approaches the normal distribution with mean μ and standard deviation $\frac{\sigma}{\sqrt{n}}$. Then:

$$P(a \le \bar{x} \le b) = P\left(\frac{a - \mu}{\frac{\sigma}{\sqrt{n}}} \le z \le \frac{b - \mu}{\frac{\sigma}{\sqrt{n}}}\right)$$

What is remarkable about this is that the **central limit theorem** says that regardless of the shape of the original distribution, the taking of averages of samples results in a normal curve. To find the distribution of $\bar{x}$, the sample means, we need to know only the original population mean and standard deviation.

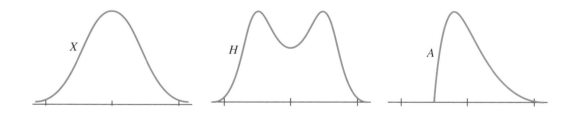

The three probability densities above all have the same mean and standard deviation. Despite their different shapes, when $n = 10$ (or more), the sampling distributions of the mean, $\bar{X}$, are nearly identical.

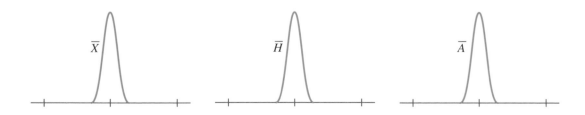

Example

The figures below illustrate two key points about the sampling distribution of a sample mean.

Figure 1 displays the distribution of customer service call lengths to a customer service centre for a week. The distribution is extremely skewed to the right (extremely positively skewed).

Figure 2 contains the lengths of a sample of (say) 60 calls from this population. If we take more samples of size 60, we will get different values for the mean. To find the sampling distribution of the mean, take many (say, 400) random samples of size 60 and calculate the mean for each sample.

Figure 2 is the distribution of the values of the mean for 400 samples.

Compare Figure 1 with Figure 2.

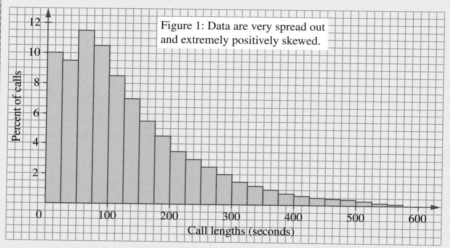

Figure 1: Data are very spread out and extremely positively skewed.

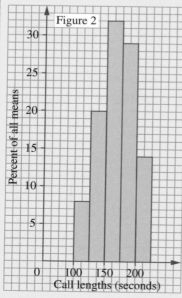

Solution: In Figure 2, the sample means are much less spread out than Figure 1. In addition, in Figure 2 the distribution is approximately symmetric, rather than skewed. In fact, the distribution is approximately normal.

key point

- Sample means are less variable than individual observations.

- Sample means are more normal than individual observations.

When taking samples, it is vital to remember:

1. The mean of the samples = The mean of the original population.

2. The standard deviation of the sample means $= \dfrac{\sigma}{\sqrt{n}}$ where σ is the standard deviation of the original population and n is the number of samples.

Why is this? Let's think about it for a minute.

Means vary less than the individual observations.

The mean age of groups of four randomly selected primary school students are shown.

Population

	Age of students				$\bar{x}$
Sample 1	5	7	11	9	8
Sample 2	10	10	12	8	10
Sample 3	6	7	9	12	$8\frac{1}{2}$
Sample 4	7	7	5	7	$6\frac{1}{2}$
Sample 5	5	12	6	6	7·25

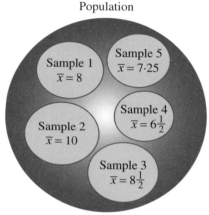

By observation, the results for $\bar{x}$, the mean of the samples, are less spread out than the individual observations.

key point

The ages of the primary school students can be randomly generated by a computer simulation.

Computer simulations

Simulation of a system is represented as the running of the system's model. It can be used to explore and gain insights into systems and to estimate the performance of complex systems.

There are many types of computer simulations. The common feature shared by all is the attempt to generate a sample of representative scenarios for a model in which a complete enumeration of all possible states of the model would be prohibitive or impossible. One of the earliest methods of simulation was developed in the 1940s by John Von Neumann and others and was called the Monte Carlo method.

Alternatively, think about this

Which would be more surprising: having one student in your class of 30 who is over 2 m tall or having the mean of 30 students in your class to be over 2 m tall? The first event is fairly rare; there may be someone in your class over 2 m tall. But finding a class of

30 students whose mean height is over 2 m tall simply will not happen! The reason is that sample means have smaller standard deviations than individuals.

It goes down by the square root of the sample size. Finally, $\dfrac{\sigma}{\sqrt{n}}$ can be reffered to as the standard error.

A particular drug gives relief from pain. The period of pain relief reported by people who are treated with the drug is normally distributed with a mean of 50 hours and standard deviation of 16 hours.

In a random sample of 64 people who have been treated with the drug, what is the probability that the mean period of pain relief reported is between 48 hours and 53 hours?

Solution

$\mu = 50$, $\sigma = 16$, $n = 64$

The standard error $= \sigma_x = \dfrac{\sigma}{\sqrt{n}} = \dfrac{16}{\sqrt{64}} = 2.$

Note: Use $z = \dfrac{x - \mu}{\sigma_x}$ twice.

If $x = 48$ then $z = \dfrac{48 - 50}{2} = -1$

If $x = 53$ then $z = \dfrac{53 - 50}{2} = 1.5$

Then $P(48 \le x \le 53) = P(-1 \le z \le 1.5)$

From the normal tables

$= 0.9332 - (1 - 0.8413)$

$= 0.7745$

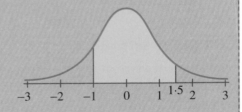

Spend some time working on the standard error, σ_x. Many candidates find it challenging.

Example

(i) The breaking strengths of cables produced by a manufacturer have a mean of 1,800 N (Newtons) and a standard deviation of 100 N. By a new technique in the manufacturing process, it is claimed that the breaking strength can be increased. To test this claim, a sample of 50 new cables is tested and it is found that their mean breaking strength is 1,825 N.

   (a) State the null hypothesis.

   (b) Is there evidence to reject or accept the null hypothesis, to a 5% level of significance?

(ii) A doctor claims that 17-year-olds have an average body temperature that is higher than the commonly accepted average adult human temperature of 37 degrees Celsius, with a standard deviation of 0·4 degrees. A simple random statistical sample of 25 people, each of age 17, is selected. The average temperature of the 17-year-olds is found to be 37·167 degrees.

   (a) State the null hypothesis.

   (b) Is there evidence to reject or accept the null hypothesis, to a 5% level of significance?

Solution

(i) (a) The null hypothesis, H_0, states the breaking strength of the cables is not increased.

   (b) The 5% level of significance $\Rightarrow z = \pm 1·96$

     The standard error for this sample is given by

$$\frac{\sigma}{\sqrt{n}} = \frac{100}{\sqrt{50}} = 14·14$$

$$z = \frac{x - \mu}{\dfrac{\sigma}{\sqrt{n}}} = \frac{1,825 - 1,800}{14·14} = 1·77$$

$$\begin{array}{c} & & & 1\cdot77 \\ \hline -1\cdot96 & & 0 & +1\cdot96 \end{array}$$

The z-score 1·77 falls inside the required confidence interval.

∴ We fail to reject the null hypothesis which is that the breaking strength of the cables is not increased.

(ii) (a) The null hypothesis, H_0, states the average temperature of 17-year-olds is the same as the average temperature of adult humans.

(b) The 5% level of significance $\Rightarrow z = \pm 1\cdot 96$

The standard error for this sample is given by

$$\frac{\sigma}{\sqrt{n}} = \frac{0\cdot 4}{\sqrt{25}} = 0\cdot 08$$

$$z = \frac{x - \mu}{\dfrac{\sigma}{\sqrt{n}}} = \frac{37\cdot 167 - 37}{0\cdot 08} = 2\cdot 0875$$

2·0875

—————————+————————————+————————|●———————————

$-1\cdot 96$ 0 $+1\cdot 96$

The z-score 2·0875 falls outside the required confidence interval.

∴ We reject the null hypothesis and conclude that the evidence indicates the average temperature of 17-year-olds is higher than the average temperature of adult humans.

(i) Assume that the duration of human pregnancies can be described by a normal model with a mean of 271 days and a standard deviation of 12 days.

  (a) What percentage of pregnancies should last between 271 and 296 days?

  (b) Using the empirical rule, write down the 95% confidence interval for the mean pregnancy duration.

  (c) Suppose a certain doctor is currently providing prenatal care to 52 pregnant women. Let $\overline{h}$ represent the mean length of their pregnancies. According to the central limit theorem, what is the distribution of this sample mean? Specify the model, mean and standard deviation.

  (d) What is the probability that the mean duration of these patients' pregnancies will be more than 275 days?

(ii) The duration of human pregnancies may not actually follow a normal model as described in part **(i)**.

  (a) Explain why it may be somewhat skewed to the left.

  (b) If the correct model is in fact skewed, does that change your answers to parts **(a)**, **(b)** and **(c)** in **(i)**? Explain why or why not for each of the three parts.

Solution

(i) (a) $P(271 \le x \le 296) = P\left(\dfrac{271 - 271}{12} \le z \le \dfrac{296 - 271}{12}\right)$

$\qquad\qquad\qquad\qquad\quad = P(0 \le z \le 2\cdot 08)$

$\qquad\qquad\qquad\qquad\quad = 0\cdot 9812 - 0\cdot 5$

$\qquad\qquad\qquad\qquad\quad = 48\%$

(b) $\pm 2 = \dfrac{x - 271}{12}$ (empirical rule ±2 standard deviations)

$271 \pm 24 = x$

247 ———————————————————— 295

(c) The distribution of these sample means is normal. Mean $\mu = 271$ and the standard deviation $\sigma_x = \dfrac{\sigma}{\sqrt{n}} = \dfrac{12}{\sqrt{52}} = 1\cdot 66$.

(d) $P(x > 275) = P\left(z > \dfrac{275 - 271}{1\cdot 66} \right) = P(z > 2\cdot 41)$

$\qquad\qquad = 1 - 0\cdot 9920$ (from normal tables)

$\qquad\qquad = 0\cdot 0080$

(ii) (a) There are not as many very long pregnancies nowadays due to births being induced after a certain stage. Hence, the curve is skewed to the left.

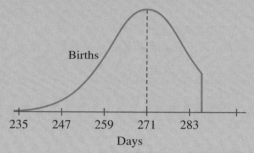

(b) For data that are significantly skewed, we cannot use the normal approximation on parts **(a)** and **(b)** in **(i)**.

However, since regardless of the initial shape of the original data the sample mean always follows a normal curve distribution, the answer for part **(i) (d)** is correct for this large sample size (52).

14 Statistics V: Confidence Intervals and Hypothesis Testing with More Accurate Margins of Error; p-Values

□ To know and understand the difference between the *approximate* formula for margin of error, $\dfrac{1}{\sqrt{n}}$, and the more accurate standard error formula from the booklet of formulae and tables.

□ To know how to calculate and apply the more accurate formulae for standard error when constructing a 95% confidence interval.

□ To apply the more accurate confidence intervals when carrying out hypothesis tests.

□ To calculate and apply the *p*-value for a test statistic as an alternative approach to hypothesis testing.

A more accurate standard error formula

The background

The **central limit theorem** in the previous chapter has introduced us to the standard error of the mean, σ_x (sometimes written $\sigma_{\bar{x}}$). When we take one sample of size n elements and calculate its proportion, $\hat{p}$, we are only finding the proportion from one of many samples of size n. If we were to consider all such proportions, we would have the **sampling distribution of the proportion**.

The standard deviation of the sampling distribution of the proportion is called the **standard error (SE) of the proportion**, written as $\sigma_{\hat{p}}$. The formula for $\sigma_{\hat{p}}$ is given in the booklet of formulae and tables as

$$\sigma_{\hat{p}} = \sqrt{\frac{p(1-p)}{n}} \quad \text{where } n \text{ is the sample size and } p \text{ is the population proportion.}$$

Hence, if the true population proportion, p, is known, we can use either the empirical rule or the standard normal tables to estimate the probability that a particular sample proportion will lie within a certain distance of the population proportion.

However, in most cases we will not know the true population proportion. This is what we are required to estimate. We reverse the process: instead of writing that there is a 95% chance that a sample proportion, $\hat{p}$, lies in the interval $[p - E, p + E]$, we write that there is a 95% chance that p, the population proportion, lies in the interval $[\hat{p} - E, \hat{p} + E]$. Hence, we use the standard error (SE) of the proportion:

$$\sigma_{\hat{p}} = \sqrt{\frac{\hat{p}(1 - \hat{p})}{n}}$$

The 95% confidence interval using the standard error

At the 95% level of confidence the value of z is: 2 using the empirical rule or 1·96 from the standard normal tables.

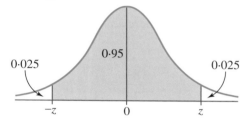

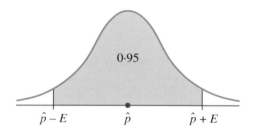

z is the number of standard deviation (SE) that the margin of error is from the mean. Hence, the margin of error, E, is given by:

$$E = (z)(\sigma_{\hat{p}})$$

At the 95% confidence interval, $E = 1·96\,\sigma_{\hat{p}}$.

We then state that the 95% confidence interval for the true proportion, p, is:

$$\hat{p} - E \leq p \leq \hat{p} + E$$

$$\hat{p} - 1·96\sqrt{\frac{\hat{p}(1 - \hat{p})}{n}} \leq p \leq \hat{p} + 1·96\sqrt{\frac{\hat{p}(1 - \hat{p})}{n}}$$

Example 1

During the making of a movie, a survey found that out of 724 extras, only 181 were suitable for parts in a major movie.

(i) Find the 95% confidence interval for the proportion of all film extras that may be suitable for parts in a major movie.

(ii) With 95% confidence, what is the highest proportion of extras who would be suitable for parts in a major movie?

(iii) If only 400 extras were surveyed.

    (a) What effect would this have on the margin of error?

    (b) Are there any implications of taking this action?

Solution

(i) $\hat{p} = \dfrac{181}{724} = \dfrac{1}{4} = 0.25 \, (= 25\%)$

$1 - \hat{p} = 1 - \dfrac{1}{4} = \dfrac{3}{4} = 0.75$

$n = 724$

Then $\sigma_{\hat{p}} = \sqrt{\dfrac{\hat{p}(1 - \hat{p})}{n}} = \sqrt{\dfrac{0.25 \times 0.75}{724}} = 0.01609279 = 0.016$

Hence, the standard error $= \text{SE} = \sigma_{\hat{p}} = 1.6\%$.

Remember, the margin of error, E, at the 95% level of confidence $= (1.96)\,\sigma_{\hat{p}} = (1.96)\,(1.6) = 3.136\% = 3.1\%$.

The 95% confidence interval for the true proportion, p, is then:

$$\hat{p} - E \le p \le \hat{p} + E$$
$$0.25 - 0.031 \le p \le 0.25 + 0.031$$
$$25\% - 3.1\% \le p \le 25\% + 3.1\%$$
$$21.9\% \le p \le 28.1\%$$

That is, the true proportion, with 95% confidence, lies between 21.9% and 28.1%.

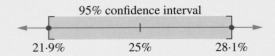

95% confidence interval

21.9%   25%   28.1%

(ii) From part (i) we are 95% confident that the highest proportion of extras who would be suitable for parts in a major movie is 28.1%.

(iii) (a) With fewer extras surveyed, the standard error would be greater,

i.e. $\sigma_{\hat{p}} = \sqrt{\dfrac{\hat{p}(1-\hat{p})}{n}} = \sqrt{\dfrac{(0\cdot25)(0\cdot75)}{400}} = 0\cdot021650635 = 0\cdot022 = 2\cdot2\%$

and $2\cdot2\% > 1\cdot6\%$. Hence, the margin of error would be greater.

(b) The new survey would be less accurate. It would be quicker and less expensive to carry out.

Example 2

A poll shows that the government's approval rating is at 70%.
The poll is based on a random sample of 896 voters with a margin of error of 3%.
Show that the poll used a 95% level of confidence.

Solution

$$\text{Confidence limits} = \pm (z)(\sigma_{\hat{p}})$$

$$0\cdot03 = \pm (z)\sqrt{\dfrac{\hat{p}(1-\hat{p})}{n}}$$

$$0\cdot03 = \pm (z)\sqrt{\dfrac{0\cdot7(1-0\cdot7)}{896}}$$

$$0\cdot03 = \pm (z)(0\cdot153)$$

$$\dfrac{0\cdot03}{0\cdot153} = \pm z$$

$$\pm 1\cdot96 = z$$

Hence, the poll is using the 95% level of confidence.

95% confidence interval for the population mean

The central limit theorem may also be applied to form a confidence interval for the mean of a population, given the mean of a large enough sample, and a standard deviation.

A population has a mean of μ and a standard deviation of σ. Suppose a sample of size $n \geq 30$ has a mean of $\bar{x}$. Then the 95% confidence interval for the population mean, μ, is:

$$\bar{x} - 1\cdot96\dfrac{\sigma}{\sqrt{n}} \leq \mu \leq \bar{x} + 1\cdot96\dfrac{\sigma}{\sqrt{n}}$$

In practice, if the standard deviation of the population, σ, is not known, then we use the standard deviation, s, of the sample in its place.

A survey was carried out to find the weekly rental costs of holiday apartments in a certain country. A random sample of 400 apartments was taken. The mean of the sample was €320 and the standard deviation was €50.

Form a 95% confidence interval for the mean weekly rental costs of holiday apartments in that country.

Solution

Let μ = the mean weekly rental of all holiday apartments. For the sample, $\bar{x} = 320$, the standard deviation $s = 50$ and $n = 400$.

We use $s = 50$ because the standard deviation, σ, of the population is not available.

SE of the mean $= \dfrac{s}{\sqrt{n}} = \dfrac{50}{\sqrt{400}} = 2.5$.

Then the 95% confidence interval for the mean weekly rental of all apartments is given by:

$$\bar{x} - 1.96\left(\frac{s}{\sqrt{n}}\right) \leq \mu \leq \bar{x} + 1.96\left(\frac{s}{\sqrt{n}}\right)$$

$$320 - 1.96(2.5) \leq \mu \leq 320 + 1.96(2.5)$$

$$315.1 \leq \mu \leq 324.9$$

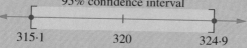

95% confidence interval

315·1   320   324·9

Hence, the 95% confidence interval for the mean weekly rental cost is from €315·10 to €324·90.

Hypothesis testing of the population proportion using the more accurate standard error

Hypothesis testing is a technique used in statistics to test whether a claim that is made is consistent with the data obtained.

You could refer back to the material on hypothesis testing in the previous chapter before tackling the next two examples.

Example 1

National data in 1970 showed that 58% of the adult population had never smoked cigarettes. In 2010, a national health survey interviewed a random sample of 880 adults and found that 52% had never smoked cigarettes.

(i) Construct a 95% confidence interval for the proportion of adults in 2010 who had never smoked cigarettes.

(ii) Does this provide evidence of a change in behaviour among the Irish?

Write appropriate hypotheses.

Using your confidence interval, test an appropriate hypothesis and state your conclusion.

Solution

(i) Use
$$\hat{p} - E \le p \le \hat{p} + E$$

where
$$\hat{p} = 52\% = 0\cdot52$$
$$1 - \hat{p} = 1 - 0\cdot52 = 0\cdot48$$
$$n = 880$$
$$z = 1\cdot96$$

Then
$$0\cdot52 - 1\cdot96\sqrt{\frac{(0\cdot52)(0\cdot48)}{880}} \le p \le 0\cdot52 + 1\cdot96\sqrt{\frac{(0\cdot52)(0\cdot48)}{880}}$$

$$0\cdot52 - 0\cdot033 \le p \le 0\cdot52 + 0\cdot033$$

$$48\cdot7\% \le p \le 55\cdot3\%$$

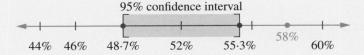

Based on these data, we are 95% confident that the proportion of adults in 2010 who had never smoked cigarettes is between 48·7% and 55·3%.

(ii) $H_0: p = 58\%$

$H_A: p \ne 58\%$

Since 58% is not in the confidence interval (see the diagram above), we reject H_0.

We conclude that the proportion of adults in 2010 who had never smoked was less than in 1970.

Example 2

A study addressed the issue of whether pregnant women can correctly guess the sex of their baby.

Among a random sample of 312 pregnant women, 171 correctly guessed the sex of the baby.

(i) Construct a 95% confidence interval from the given data.

(ii) Use these sample data to test the claim, at the 5% level of significance, that the success rate of such guesses is no different from the 50% success rate expected with random chance guesses.

Solution

(i) $\hat{p} = \dfrac{171}{312} = 0{\cdot}548 \,(= 54{\cdot}8\%)$

$1 - \hat{p} = 1 - 0{\cdot}548 = 0{\cdot}452$

$n = 312$

$z = 1{\cdot}96$

Use

$$\hat{p} - E \leq p \leq \hat{p} + E$$

$$0{\cdot}548 - 1{\cdot}96\sqrt{\dfrac{(0{\cdot}548)(0{\cdot}452)}{312}} \leq p \leq 0{\cdot}548 + 1{\cdot}96\sqrt{\dfrac{(0{\cdot}548)(0{\cdot}452)}{312}}$$

$$0{\cdot}548 - 0{\cdot}055 \leq p \leq 0{\cdot}548 + 0{\cdot}055$$

$$0{\cdot}493 \leq p \leq 0{\cdot}603$$

$$49{\cdot}3\% \leq p \leq 60{\cdot}3\%$$

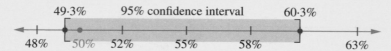

Based on the given data, we are 95% confident that the proportion of pregnant women who correctly predicted the sex of their baby was between 49·3% and 60·3%.

(ii) H_0, the null hypothesis: the success rate is no different from 50%.

$H_0: p = 0{\cdot}5 = 50\%$

$H_A: p \neq 0{\cdot}5$

As 50% is included in the confidence interval above we fail to reject the null hypothesis.

Hence, we conclude that there is not sufficient evidence to warrant rejection of the claim that women can correctly guess the sex of their baby.

In the final analysis, testing the null hypothesis, H_0, simply involves a confidence interval and a red dot.

Either	Or
Confidence interval	Confidence interval
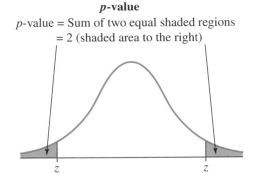	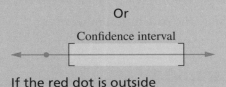
If the red dot is inside the confidence interval, we fail to reject H_0.	If the red dot is outside the confidence interval, we reject H_0.

p-Values: An alternative approach to hypothesis testing

A p-value is:

- a probability
- used to make a decision on the null hypothesis, H_0
- a measure of the strength of evidence to reject or fail to reject the null hypothesis.

p-value

p-value = Sum of two equal shaded regions
= 2 (shaded area to the right)

Critical values for R
(at the 5% level of significance)

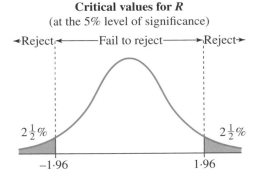

The decision to reject, or fail to reject, H_0 is based on the comparison of the p-value with the level of significance. On our course we only use a two-tailed test at the 5% level of significance.

It is vital to know that the critical p-value $= 0.05$ at the 5% significance level.

If $p \leq 0.05$, there is strong evidence to reject H_0.

If $p > 0.05$, there is strong evidence to fail to reject H_0.

How to perform a hypothesis test using p-value

1. State H_0 and H_A.
2. Calculate the z score (this is often called the test statistic, T).
3. Determine the p-value (a diagram is useful).
4. If $p \le 0.05$, reject H_0. If $p > 0.05$, fail to reject H_0.
5. State the conclusion in words.

Example 1

A machine produces metal rods which have a mean length of 500 cm with a standard deviation of 4 cm. After a service to the machine, it is claimed that the machine now produces rods with lengths that are not equal to 500 cm. To test the claim, a random sample of 100 rods from the serviced machine are measured and found to have a mean length of 500·5 cm.

(i) Write down H_0 and H_A.

(ii) Calculate the test statistic for this sample mean.

(iii) Calculate a p-value for this sample mean.

(iv) At the 5% level of significance, is there evidence to show that the mean length of the metal rod from the serviced machine is not 500 cm? Justify your answer.

Solution

(i) The null hypothesis, H_0: $\mu = 500$ cm.

The alternative hypothesis, H_A: $\mu \ne 500$ cm.

(ii) $\bar{x} = 500·5$, $\mu = 500$, $\sigma = 4$ and $n = 100$

The test statistic is given by:

$$T = \frac{\bar{x} - \mu}{\dfrac{\sigma}{\sqrt{n}}} = \frac{500·5 - 500}{\dfrac{4}{\sqrt{100}}} = 1·25$$

(iii) $p(T > 1 \cdot 25)$

$= 1 - P(z \leq 1 \cdot 25)$

$= 1 - 0 \cdot 8944$ (from tables)

$= 0 \cdot 1056$

The p-value $= 2\,(0 \cdot 1056)$

$= 0 \cdot 2112$

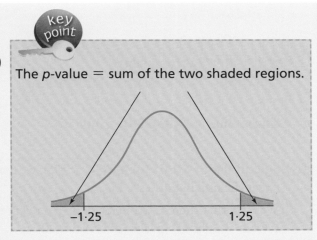

key point

The p-value = sum of the two shaded regions.

−1·25   1·25

(iv) Since $0 \cdot 2112 > 0 \cdot 05$ (or $21 \cdot 12\% > 5\%$), we conclude there is strong evidence not to reject the null hypothesis

We state that we fail to reject the claim that the mean length of the metal rods from the serviced machines is not 500 cm.

Example 2

A company claims that the average weight of a packet of cereal it produces is 400 g with a standard deviation of 12 g. To test this claim, a random sample of 64 of these packets were weighed and found to have a mean value of 403 g.

(i) Write down H_0 and H_A.

(ii) Calculate the test statistic for this sample mean.

(iii) Calculate a p-value for this sample mean.

(iv) At the 5% level of significance, is there evidence to show that the mean weight of the packets of cereal is not 400 g? Justify your answer.

Solution

(i) The null hypothesis, H_0: $\mu = 400$ g

The alternative hypothesis, H_A: $\mu \neq 400$ g.

(ii) $\bar{x} = 403$, $\mu = 400$, $\sigma = 12$ and $n = 64$

The test statistic is given by:

$$T = \frac{\bar{x} - \mu}{\dfrac{\sigma}{\sqrt{n}}} = \frac{403 - 400}{\dfrac{12}{\sqrt{64}}} = 2$$

(iii) $P(T > 2)$

$= 1 - P(z \leq 2)$

$= 1 - 0.9772$ (from tables)

$= 0.0228$

The p-value $= 2(0.0228) = 0.0456$

(iv) Since $0.0456 < 0.05$ (or $4.56\% < 5\%$), we conclude there is strong evidence to reject the null hypothesis, H_0.

We state that there is strong evidence to reject the claim by the company that the average weight of a packet of cereal is 400 g.

exam focus

- If p is low, H_0 must go.
- The lower the p-value, the stronger the evidence against H_0.
- The larger the sample size, the more precise the estimate.

Glossary of Statistical Terms

Arithmetic mean A measure of central tendency that sums all the scores in the data sets and divides by the number of scores.

Asymptotic The quality of the normal curve such that the tails never touch the horizontal axis.

Bell-shaped curve (normal curve) A distribution of scores that is symmetrical about the mean, median and mode and has asymptotic tails.

Bias Systematic errors in the way the sample represents the population. It can be caused by poorly worded surveys, non-response or undercoverage.

Bimodal A bimodal data set (distribution) has two peaks of data, as in the diagram below.

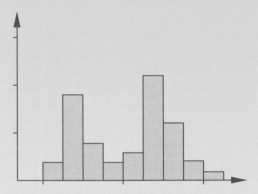

Bivariate data A survey that examines the relationship between two variables (data sets). In our course, the two variables are usually quantitative variables.

Categorical data Non-numerical data that can be counted but only described in words. Such data may be ordered or unordered.

Causality The relationship between an event (the cause) and a second event (the effect).

Class interval The upper and lower boundary of a set of scores used in the creation of a frequency distribution.

Confidence interval A range around a measurement that conveys how precise the measurement is.

Confidence level A measure of the reliability of a result. A confidence level of 95% (0·95) means we are 95% sure the result is reliable. Some confusion is caused by the use of the term 5% level to represent the 95% level.

Continuous numerical data Data which can take any numerical value within a certain range.

Correlation coefficient (r) A numerical index that reflects the relationship between two variables, constant between -1 and 1.

Critical value The value necessary for rejection (or non-acceptance) of the null hypothesis.

Cumulative frequency distribution A frequency distribution that shows frequencies for class intervals along with the cumulative frequency for each.

Data An item, or items, of factual information derived from measurement or research.

Data point An observation.

Data set A set of data points.

Dependent variable Often denoted by y, whose value depends on another variable. It is usually represented on the vertical axis.

Descriptive statistics Values that describe the characteristics of a sample or population.

Direct correlation A positive correlation where the values of both variables change in the same direction.

Discrete numerical data Data which can only have certain values.

Frequency distribution A method for illustrating the distribution of scores within class intervals. Often given in tabular form (frequency distribution table).

Frequency polygon A graphical representation of a frequency distribution.

Histogram A graphical representation of a frequency distribution.

Hypothesis An if–then statement of conjecture that relates variables to one another.

Independent variable Often denoted by x, whose variation does not depend on another variable. It is usually represented on the horizontal axis.

Indirect correlation A negative correlation where the values of variables move in opposite directions.

Inferential statistics Tools that are used to infer the results based on a sample to a population.

Line of best fit (regression line) The line that best fits the actual scores and minimises the error in prediction.

Margin of error The extent of the interval on either side of the sample proportion.

Mean The value where scores are summed and divided by the number of observations.

Measures of central tendency The mean, median and mode.

Median The point at which 50% of the cases in a distribution fall below and 50% fall above.

Mid-interval value The central value in a class interval.

Mode The most frequently occurring score in a distribution.

Multimodal A distribution is said to be multimodal if it has three or more peaks.

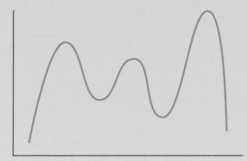

Normal curve See *bell-shaped curve*. See also the diagram below.

Null hypothesis (H₀) The statement being tested in a test of significance is called the null hypothesis. The test of significance is designed to assess the strength of the evidence against the null hypothesis. Usually the null hypothesis is a statement of 'no effect' or 'no difference'.

Observed score The score that is recorded or observed.

Obtained value The value that results from the application of a statistical test.

One-tailed test Applies when interested only in extreme values on one side of the mean, i.e. one tail of the distribution.

Outliers Those scores in a distribution that are noticeably much more extreme than the majority of scores. Exactly what score is an outlier is usually an arbitrary decision made by the researcher.

Parameter The term used to identify a characteristic, feature or measureable factor that can help understand/interpret a particular system.

Percentile point The point at or below where a score appears.

Platykurtic The quality of a normal curve that defines its flatness.

Population All the possible subjects or cases of interest.

Predictor The variable that predicts an outcome.

Primary data First-hand data that you collect yourself or are collected by someone under your direct supervision.

Qualitative data A type of information that describes or characterises, but does not measure, data. Often referred to as non-numerical data.

Quantitative data A type of information that can be counted or expressed numerically.

Range The highest score minus the lowest score.

Reliability The quality of a test such that it is consistent.

Sample A subset of a population.

Sampling error The difference between sample and population values.

Scatter plot A plot of paired data points.

Secondary data Second-hand data that have already been collected and made available from an external source such as newspapers, government departments or the internet.

Significance level The risk set by the researcher for rejecting a null hypothesis when it is true.

Skew or skewness The quality of a distribution that defines the disproportionate frequency of certain scores. A longer right tail than left corresponds to a smaller number of occurrences at the high end of the distribution; this is a *positively* skewed distribution. A shorter right tail than left corresponds to a larger number of occurrences at the high end of the distribution; this is a *negatively* skewed distribution.

Standard deviation (σ) A measure of dispersion (spread) of a set of values from their mean.

Standard error The standard deviation of the sample means $\left(\dfrac{\sigma}{\sqrt{n}} \right)$.

Standard score See *Z-score*.

Statistics A set of tools and techniques used to collect, organise, represent and interpret information.

Two-tailed test A test that applies when interested in the corresponding Z-score on both sides of the mean, i.e. both tails of the distribution. Sometimes called two-sided tests. See the diagram below.

Type I error The probability of rejecting a null hypothesis when it is true.

Type II error   The probability of accepting a null hypothesis when it is false.

Unbiased estimate   A conservative estimate of a population parameter.

Unimodal   A unimodal data set (distribution) has one peak of data. See the diagram below.

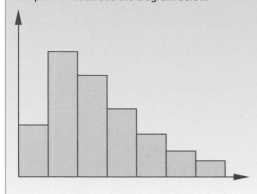

Univariate data   A survey that looks at only one variable (data set). The variable may be either qualitative or quantitative.

Validity   The quality of a test such that it measures what it says it does.

Variability   The amount of spread or dispersion in a set of scores.

Variance   The square of the standard deviation, and another measure of a distribution's spread or dispersion.

Z-score   Indicates the number of standard deviations that a value is above or below the mean:

$$z = \frac{x - \mu}{\sigma}$$

The Normal Curve Tables

**Dóchúlachtaí don
dáileadh normalach caighdeánach**

I gcás z a thugtar, faightear ón tábla

$$P(Z \leq z) = \frac{1}{\sqrt{2\pi}} \int_{-\infty}^{z} e^{-\frac{1}{2}t^2} dt$$

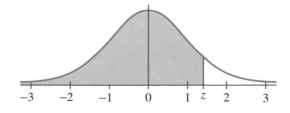

**Probabilities for the standard normal
distribution**

For a given z, the table gives

$$P(Z \leq z) = \frac{1}{\sqrt{2\pi}} \int_{-\infty}^{z} e^{-\frac{1}{2}t^2} dt$$

z	0·00	0·01	0·02	0·03	0·04	0·05	0·06	0·07	0·08	0·09
0·0	0·5000	·5040	·5080	·5120	·5160	·5199	·5239	·5279	·5319	·5359
0·1	0·5398	·5438	·5478	·5517	·5557	·5596	·5636	·5675	·5714	·5753
0·2	0·5793	·5832	·5871	·5910	·5948	·5987	·6026	·6064	·6103	·6141
0·3	0·6179	·6217	·6255	·6293	·6331	·6368	·6406	·6443	·6480	·6517
0·4	0·6554	·6591	·6628	·6664	·6700	·6736	·6772	·6808	·6844	·6879
0·5	0·6915	·6950	·6985	·7019	·7054	·7088	·7123	·7157	·7190	·7224
0·6	0·7257	·7291	·7324	·7357	·7389	·7422	·7454	·7486	·7517	·7549
0·7	0·7580	·7611	·7642	·7673	·7704	·7734	·7764	·7794	·7823	·7852
0·8	0·7881	·7910	·7939	·7967	·7995	·8023	·8051	·8078	·8106	·8133
0·9	0·8159	·8186	·8212	·8238	·8264	·8289	·8315	·8340	·8365	·8389
1·0	0·8413	·8438	·8461	·8485	·8508	·8531	·8554	·8577	·8599	·8621
1·1	0·8643	·8665	·8686	·8708	·8729	·8749	·8770	·8790	·8810	·8830
1·2	0·8849	·8869	·8888	·8907	·8925	·8944	·8962	·8980	·8997	·9015
1·3	0·9032	·9049	·9066	·9082	·9099	·9115	·9131	·9147	·9162	·9177
1·4	0·9192	·9207	·9222	·9236	·9251	·9265	·9279	·9292	·9306	·9319
1·5	0·9332	·9345	·9357	·9370	·9382	·9394	·9406	·9418	·9429	·9441
1·6	0·9452	·9463	·9474	·9484	·9495	·9505	·9515	·9525	·9535	·9545
1·7	0·9554	·9564	·9573	·9582	·9591	·9599	·9608	·9616	·9625	·9633
1·8	0·9641	·9649	·9656	·9664	·9671	·9678	·9686	·9693	·9699	·9706
1·9	0·9713	·9719	·9726	·9732	·9738	·9744	·9750	·9756	·9761	·9767
2·0	0·9772	·9778	·9783	·9788	·9793	·9798	·9803	·9808	·9812	·9817
2·1	0·9821	·9826	·9830	·9834	·9838	·9842	·9846	·9850	·9854	·9857
2·2	0·9861	·9864	·9868	·9871	·9875	·9878	·9881	·9884	·9887	·9890
2·3	0·9893	·9896	·9898	·9901	·9904	·9906	·9909	·9911	·9913	·9916
2·4	0·9918	·9920	·9922	·9925	·9927	·9929	·9931	·9932	·9934	·9936
2·5	0·9938	·9940	·9941	·9943	·9945	·9946	·9948	·9949	·9951	·9952
2·6	0·9953	·9955	·9956	·9957	·9959	·9960	·9961	·9962	·9963	·9964
2·7	0·9965	·9966	·9967	·9968	·9969	·9970	·9971	·9972	·9973	·9974
2·8	0·9974	·9975	·9976	·9977	·9977	·9978	·9979	·9979	·9980	·9981
2·9	0·9981	·9982	·9982	·9983	·9984	·9984	·9985	·9985	·9986	·9986
3·0	0·9987	·9987	·9987	·9988	·9988	·9989	·9989	·9989	·9990	·9990

Calculator Instructions

Casio Natural Display Calculator

Before starting any procedures on the calculator, you should clear the memory:

To clear the memory:

Shift + 9 : CLR

3 : All

= : Yes

To find mean and standard deviation

To perform statistical calculations, we must create a frequency table.

To enter a frequency table, you must switch Frequency on:

Shift + Mode : Setup

Down Arrow

3 : STAT

1 : ON

To enter a table of data:

Mode

2 : STAT

1 : 1-VAR

Enter the data into the table, followed by the = sign each time. Once you have finished entering the data press:

AC button.

To analyse the data in the table:

Shift + 1 : STAT

4 : Var

Options are as follows:

$2 : \bar{x}$ (the mean of the terms, also known as μ)

$3 : \sigma x$ (the standard deviation)

For simplicity, to find the mean or standard deviation of a **single list of data**, create a frequency table and set all the frequencies to 1.

To find correlation coefficient, *r*

You must switch Frequency off:

Shift + Mode : Setup

Down Arrow

3 : STAT

2 : OFF

To enter a table of bivariate data:

Mode

2 : STAT

2 : A + BX

Enter the data into the table, followed by the = sign each time. Once you have finished entering the data press:

AC button.

To analyse the data in the table:

Shift + 1 : STAT

5 : Reg

Options are as follows:

3 : *r* (the correlation coefficient)

The line of best fit can be written as: $y = A + Bx$

The values of *A* and *B* can be found on the calculator, in the same menu as correlation coefficient: 1 : *A*   2 : *B*

Sharp WriteView Calculator

Before starting any procedures on the calculator, you should clear the memory:

To clear the memory:

2nd F + ALPHA : M-CLR

1 : Memory

0 : Clear

To find mean and standard deviation

To put the calculator into Statistics mode:

Mode

1 : STAT

0 : SD

To enter the data:

Take each value and frequency as a pair of data.

Enter each pair, separated by a comma

Then press the DATA button

(e.g. enter: 2 , 13 DATA)

Once all the pairs of data have been entered, press:

ON / C

To analyse the data entered:

ALPHA then 4 then $=$: $\bar{x}$ (the mean of the terms, also known as μ)

ALPHA then 6 then $=$: σx (the standard deviation)

To find correlation coefficient, *r*

To put the calculator into Statistics mode:

Mode
1 : STAT
1 : LINE

To enter the data:

Take each value and frequency as a pair of data.

Enter each pair, separated by a comma
Then press the DATA button
(e.g. enter: 2 , 13 DATA)

Once all the pairs of data have been entered, press:

ON / C

To analyse the data entered:

ALPHA then $\div$ then $=$: r
(the correlation coefficient)

Practice exercise

Use your calculator to find the mean and standard deviation of the following table of data:

Value	2	4	6	8	10
Frequency	13	6	9	2	6

The answers are:

$$\text{Mean } \mu = \bar{x} = 5 \qquad \text{Standard Deviation } \sigma x = 2 \cdot 88675$$

Practice exercise

Use your calculator to find the correlation coefficient and the line of best fit of the following bivariate data:

Value X	1	2	4	6	9
Frequency Y	7	9	6	3	8

The answers are:

$$\text{Correlation coefficient } r = -0 \cdot 209785$$
$$\text{Line of best fit: } \quad y = 7 \cdot 26 - 0 \cdot 15\, x$$